REMEMBER TO KILL ME

REMEMBER TO KILL ME

A Pierre Chambrun Mystery Novel

Hugh Pentecost

DODD, MEAD & COMPANY
New York

Published by Dodd, Mead & Company, Inc.
79 Madison Avenue, New York, N.Y. 10016
Distributed in Canada by
McClelland and Stewart Limited, Toronto
Manufactured in the United States of America
Designed by Stanley S. Drate
First Edition

Library of Congress Cataloging in Publication Data

Pentecost, Hugh, 1903–
    Remember to kill me.

    I. Title.
PS3531.H442R4   1984   813'.52   83-25323
ISBN 0-396-08309-9

PART
ONE

1

It was a moment of such shocking violence that I couldn't have imagined it in my wildest nightmare. It turned my world, which is the Beaumont, New York's top luxury hotel, into a bloody shambles. A person very dear to me escaped being murdered as a result of what I can only call three miracles.

Where to begin? I suppose I should start by identifying myself. I am Mark Haskell, the public relations man for the Beaumont and have been for the last ten years or so. The disaster that overtook us that summer night began, I suppose I could say, almost a year ago when Diana Ross, the glamorous pop singer, gave a free concert in Central Park. Believe it or not, some eight hundred thousand people turned out for that event. That number of people is hard to believe but I got a look at them from the roof of the Beaumont and I can only tell you that it looked like an ocean of people. Miss Ross had only just begun to sing when a violent thunderstorm hit the city and that section of the park. Standing in the rain, Miss Ross announced that she would sing the next night and thousands of people scrambled for cover, in the subways, in the lobbies of neighboring buildings, covering themselves with whatever they had, like blankets they'd brought to spread on the grass or trash bags. Some just had to laugh philosophically and let themselves be drenched.

The next night the crowd was smaller—only three hundred and fifty thousand people! The outcome was even more of a catastrophe. An army of young goons armed with baseball bats and knives—and some of them with guns—swarmed among the concertgoers, stealing jewelry and money and anything else of value people had on them. Having mugged Miss Ross's audience, they headed downtown from Columbus Circle into the Times Square area, attacking and robbing the exiting theater audiences.

It was a citywide scandal. Hadn't there been enough police? Only forty arrests were made, with more than a thousand police assigned to cover the event. Should there be any more free concerts in the park? The debate raged hot and heavy for months. In the end it was decided to give it another try, and Donna Ward, one of the newest pop stars, appeared before another huge crowd.

Pierre Chambrun, the legendary manager of the Beaumont and my boss, wasn't asleep to the possibility of trouble. People in that crowd might choose to invade his hotel for drinks at the famous Trapeze Bar, the Spartan Room, and the Blue Lagoon, the hotel's glamorous nightclub. Our security staff, headed by Jerry Dodd, a wiry, intense former FBI agent, was mobilized. Both the day and night forces were on duty to deal with any noisy drunks who might come aboard. No one could have imagined in advance what did happen.

There was peace in the park, but shortly after the concert ended, bands of young thugs, armed as before with clubs, knives, and guns, charged the three main entrances to our hotel, plus the basement garage and the service entrances. The result was wild hysteria as guests in the

4

lobby, the bars, and the nightclub were shoved around, beaten, and robbed. Vandalism was rampant. Pictures on the wall were smashed; so were glassware and liquor behind the bars. Dozens of them raced for the stairways to invade the upper floors of the hotel and rob the guests in their rooms. Jerry Dodd's small army of forty men were almost helpless. They couldn't use the guns they were authorized to carry for fear of shooting innocent guests who were struggling to get away to safety. It was a total horror.

Pierre Chambrun, alerted, ordered all power to the elevators shut off and ordered Dodd's men to block the stairways. Quite a few of the invaders had already gotten upstairs in the hotel, but with Jerry Dodd's men stationed in the stairways and the elevators not running, those few wouldn't get away. Two of them tried and were winged by Dodd's men. It was safe to use guns there because there were no guests in the line of fire.

The police came, late but finally effective. The Beaumont's lobby, bars, and nightclub looked as if they had been struck by a tornado. Emergency medical help was treating wounded guests and even some of the goons.

Police and some of Jerry Dodd's men were searching the upper floors for any of the young thugs who might not yet have been caught or fled. I remember suddenly seeing Pierre Chambrun, standing in the middle of the lobby, which was littered with broken glass, smashed furniture, and wounded and sometimes moaning guests. I have said somewhere that Chambrun reminds me of that great, late actor Claude Rains—short, stocky, capable of humor and wit, and also capable of being cold and hard as a hanging judge. That night I thought he looked like a general surveying the scene of a lost battle. How do you recoup the loss? How do you get revenge for a bitter defeat?

5

I was just approaching him for orders when Mike Maggio, the night bell captain, came running up to him. He was holding a handkerchief to a bloody wound at the side of his forehead. Mike is a dark, bright-eyed young man, born street-wise. He'd obviously not backed away from an encounter with the attackers.

"Someone has tried to murder Mrs. Haven," Mike told The Man. Most of us call Chambrun "The Man."

"Get the elevators running," Chambrun said. Even he couldn't face climbing forty flights of stairs. To hell with whether someone got away. Mrs. Victoria Haven mattered a great deal to him.

There are three penthouses on the roof of the Beaumont. One of them is occupied by Chambrun, The Man; one is reserved for very special guests, usually foreign diplomats in New York on United Nations business; the middle one, sold as a condominium when the hotel was first launched more than forty years ago, is owned and occupied by a fabulous lady. Fifty years or more ago Victoria Haven was a famous international beauty. There are rumors of romances with the most famous men of her time. Today, at eighty-four, she is still an extraordinarily handsome and vigorous woman. I have heard a whisper here and there that forty years ago there had been a young-man-older-woman romance with Pierre Chambrun. True or not, I know that today he considers her a valued and cherished friend.

When we reached the roof in a re-activated elevator, Chambrun and I, along with Jerry Dodd, our security chief, heard the story of the three miracles I have mentioned earlier.

Mrs. Haven had been fascinated by the huge crowds of people gathered in the park across the way to listen to

Donna Ward. Mrs. Haven had walked out of the little fenced-in garden behind her penthouse and over to the high parapet that surrounded the roof. She was a tall woman, just tall enough to see over the high wall and down at the sea of people across the avenue in the park. Miss Ward's performance was amplified through loudspeakers, and Mrs. Haven could hear her quite clearly. The girl was really good, Mrs. Haven told herself.

When the concert ended and the crowd in the park began to drift away Mrs. Haven suddenly realized that she'd been standing, watching and listening, for a good two hours. She started back for her penthouse, complaining, she told us later, about her "damned old bones." She felt painfully stiff as she let herself into her fenced-in garden. It was a beautiful night, stars and moon, and she sat down in a wicker garden chair, stretching her still rather handsome legs to get her circulation going again.

That was when it happened. There was the sound of a gunshot and Mrs. Haven felt a sudden searing pain. That was the first miracle. The bullet tore through the flesh on the inner side of the lady's upper left arm. Just a few inches to the left it would have gone straight through her heart and that would have been that.

The second miracle was that this old lady moved with astonishing speed and almost unbelievable foresight. She dove out of her chair and rolled over to the flower bed against the fence, face down. Two more bullets plowed into the fence not a foot above her head. Had she stood up to run the gunman would have taken her down with ease.

The third miracle came from an unexpected source. Mrs. Haven always referred to her constant companion in the penthouse as "my Japanese gentleman friend." He was a little black-and-white Japanese spaniel with a nasty disposi-

7

tion except for his mistress who was the love of his life. His name was Toto, and when the second and third shots had been fired he set up an outcry of rage and fear at an ear-piercing level. Toto's outcry brought the occupant of the guest penthouse out onto the roof. He was Sir George Brooks, an English diplomat in town on a mission to the UN. There couldn't have been anyone better in the world to take care of Mrs. Haven in her emergency. Sir George Brooks had once been a Scotland Yard detective, knighted for bravery above and beyond the call of duty. He had, I found out later, saved the Queen from an attack by a would-be assassin in Buckingham Palace.

Brooks was not a stranger to gunshot wounds, and he got Mrs. Haven into her penthouse and called for just the right help. When Chambrun and Jerry Dodd and I got there, Mrs. Haven was already being cared for by Dr. Partridge, the Beaumont's house physician. Toto and Sir George Brooks had to be considered that third miracle.

Victoria Haven was stretched out on the couch in her cluttered living room being tended to by Dr. Partridge when we arrived. I say "cluttered" because Mrs. Haven's apartment looked like a residence for the famous Collier brothers—books, papers, and magazines scattered everywhere and piled in stacks. It appeared to be total confusion until you looked closer and saw that there wasn't a speck of dust anywhere. "A storehouse for her memories," Chambrun once told me. "Those memories are more precious to her than priceless paintings, or draperies or antiques."

She looked up at Chambrun and gave him a wry smile. I thought it probably helped to cover what must have been considerable pain.

"It seems, Pierre, that someone chose me for target practice," she said.

Chambrun's hanging-judge look was tempered by a genuine anxiety for his friend. "Doctor?" he asked.

"Flesh wound," Dr. Partridge said. "No muscles or bones hurt. A couple of inches to the left . . ." He shrugged.

The tall gray-haired man standing to one side whom I realized was Sir George Brooks chipped in, "If the lady hadn't been quick-witted enough to take cover, the second shots would almost certainly have been fatal. I didn't hear any shots—my penthouse is soundproofed, air-conditioned. But if that blessed little dog hadn't raised such a racket, I wouldn't have known anything had happened." He reached down to pat the dog's head and Toto snarled at him. That was Toto for you.

"You're not hurt anywhere else, Victoria?" Chambrun asked.

"I'm not hurt physically, Pierre. I'm a little hurt that someone wanted to do me in."

"We didn't know what was going on downstairs," Brooks said. "The lady didn't know, or she wouldn't have been sitting out in her garden, looking at the stars. If she had known the hotel was overrun by violent looters, she'd have been inside with her doors locked!"

"This gunman must have been one of the first ones in," Jerry Dodd said. "Commandeered an elevator and got up here before we had the power shut off."

"I suppose he thought people who lived on the roof might have something worth stealing." Brooks glanced around Mrs. Haven's disorderly living room. "You have anything of real value here, Mrs. Haven?"

"Only about a half-million dollars' worth of jewelry," Jerry Dodd said.

Brook's eyes widened. "Just here—loose?"

"I've never thought it made any sense to have beautiful trinkets locked away in a safe where you couldn't enjoy them. I've lived in this penthouse for forty-one years, Sir George, and no one has ever stolen so much as a postage stamp from me. Mr. Dodd runs a tight ship."

"Tonight was different," Jerry Dodd said grimly.

"You didn't see anyone when you came out on the roof, Sir George?" Chambrun asked.

"Only this bloody little dog, screaming his head off."

Chambrun turned to the doctor. "Shouldn't we get Mrs. Haven down to the hospital unit?"

"I'm staying here, Pierre," the old lady said. "Dr. Partridge has stopped the bleeding. That's all there is to it. I don't want some silly nurse poking around at me."

"This killer could still be somewhere around the upper floors," Jerry Dodd said. "The power was off by the time he tried to go down. We're going to have to go over the whole place, room by room, anyway. Unless you need me here?"

"Go," Chambrun said.

"What puzzled me," Sir George Brooks said as Jerry left us, "is why this man tried to kill Mrs. Haven. He could have handled her, ransacked the place, and not risked facing charges for a major crime."

Chambrun gave the Englishman a bleak look. "I've been asking myself the same question," he said.

It was after midnight when we left Mrs. Haven. I was about to say "alone," but that would have been only a figure of speech. Her friends left her, including Dr. Partridge, who was needed to care for the dozens of people who'd been injured by the invading hoodlums. But Mrs. Haven wasn't, technically, alone. In spite of the fact that we needed every security man available to comb the hotel for invaders who might have sifted to the upper levels, Chambrun ordered three men to guard the old lady, one to stay in the penthouse with her, and two to patrol the roof outside.

I can't begin to describe the scene of destruction, the hysteria and confusion, that greeted us when Chambrun and I got back to the lobby. The destruction done to furnishings and decorations made the place look like a disaster area after a storm. Everywhere, police doctors and a couple of nurses from our hospital were helping people who'd received minor injuries. Outside the wail of ambulance sirens indicated that others had been more seriously hurt. Police were everywhere—and the press! The moment Chambrun appeared he was surrounded by a horde of reporters and TV camera crews shouting questions at him.

Chambrun held up his arms for silence and got as much as was possible.

"I will hold a press conference in the grand ballroom in an hour," he told them, "circumstances permitting. Right now there are more important things to do than talk, as you must see for yourselves."

I was left to handle them. I felt as though I was caught in the middle of a whirlpool. I knew a lot of these people, but suddenly they seemed like a pack of hungry animals.

"I don't know much more than you do," I tried to tell them. "It was like a dam breaking. They seemed to come from everywhere."

"You weren't prepared for trouble?"

"Not this kind of trouble," I told them. "We had extra men on, thinking we might attract a few stray drunks. But this! There must have been two or three hundred of them!"

"We heard there was a shooting up in the roof, Mark." That was Jack Wilson, the International News man, an old friend.

"One of them got up there before we got the elevators

11

shut down," I told him. "He did some wild shooting. Victoria Haven was hit." I was aware he knew Mrs. Haven.

"Badly hurt?"

"No, fortunately."

"Can we go up to talk to her?"

"Not yet. As you can imagine, the lady is in shock." Which was a bald lie. Mrs. Haven wasn't nearly as much in shock as I was.

"Some of the creeps are still in the hotel?" Wilson asked.

"We're afraid so. We don't know yet how much damage there is or how many people may be hurt upstairs. When Chambrun talks to you, he'll have more facts and figures. You've got to give us a little air for a while, friends."

I had something else on my mind. As I've said somewhere else, I am always in love forever—every three months. Right now there was a lady working in the Blue Lagoon who was my forever dream of the moment. I wanted to find out if she was okay. Sally Mills is a beautiful blonde who's been acting as a hostess in the nightclub for the last few months.

The Blue Lagoon had been hit hard by the attackers. Mr. Cardoza, the club's captain, greeted me at the entrance. Someone had placed an adhesive patch on a cut over his right eye.

He gave me a bitter little smile. "You don't look as if you'd been in the middle of things, Mark," he said.

"I guess I got lucky." I was looking past him into the wreck of his nightclub, tables overturned, glassware and china shattered, the grand piano on the stage splintered. "Sally?" I asked him.

His smile tightened at the corners. "One of those goons tried to rape her, right there on the stage in front of my hysterical customers," Cardoza said. He touched the adhesive on his forehead. "That's how I got this—trying to help her."

"My God! Where is she?"

"Backstage, in one of the dressing rooms. It didn't happen to her, Mark, but she was pretty roughly handled."

I didn't wait for more. I stumbled across the destroyed room, up onto the stage, and back into the dressing room area, calling out Sally's name.

I found her, lying on a chaise longue, in the star's dressing room. Hilary Foster, the star of that week's show in the Lagoon, was sitting beside her, holding a wet towel to Sally's face.

"Sally!"

She turned her head slightly. Her mouth was swollen and there was a dark bruise under one eye.

"For God's sake go away, Mark," she said, her voice rough and strained. "Unless you enjoy looking at raw hamburger."

I knelt down beside her and took her hands in mine. Her fingers gripped me so tightly I might have been going to save her from drowning.

"Oh, Mark!" she whispered. "That animal having at me . . . If it hadn't been for Mr. Cardoza—"

I had never felt such a hot rage in my whole life. "Can you describe him?" I asked her. "Because I'm going to kill him."

"Oh, I can describe him," Sally said. "Every inch of his ugly face, his stained teeth, the wicked, hungry gleam in his eyes!"

"I think we should all just consider ourselves lucky that nothing worse happened to any of us," Hilary Foster said in a quiet voice. "I could identify that thug if I ever saw him again, but I think we should just thank God for Sally that he didn't get what he was after."

"He—he dragged me up on stage," Sally said, a little breathless. "He—he started to tear off my clothes. I tried to fight him off, but he hit me back and forth across the face with the back of his hairy hand. I was too groggy to fight any more, and then Mr. Cardoza was there. He had a carving knife from the buffet, and he slashed at this character with it. The man is wounded, if we ever find him!"

"He hit Mr. Cardoza with a candlestick he picked up off the piano," Hilary said. "But then he took off, clutching at his shoulder where Mr. Cardoza had knifed him. I could see the blood trickling out between his fingers."

"I'll find him, if I have to search every dive in the city," I said.

Hilary Foster stood up. She gave me a sympathetic smile. "Just take Sally somewhere she can be quiet," she said, "out of all this confusion. The police may have picked up your man when he tried to get away. That means you can deal with him legally."

"I don't give a damn about legal!" I said, and realized I was being pretty loud-mouthed about my heroism.

"I have friends who need to be told I'm safe," Hilary said. "Take care of her, Mark." She bent down, touched Sally's naked shoulder where her dress had been torn away, and left.

"They took all her jewelry," Sally told me as Hilary left. "It was stage stuff, but it looked expensive." She was still hanging onto me for dear life.

"I can't kiss you, because it would hurt you," I said. "Let me take you up to my apartment. You'll be perfectly safe

14

there." I grinned at her. "You've got a robe up there, and you can get the touch of that creep washed off you."

I helped her up. She was pretty unsteady on her feet.

"Can't we go up the service way?" she asked me. "I don't want people to see me like this." She touched the torn front of her dress.

"It'll be safer the front way, and you'll only be one in a crowd. They mauled a hell of a lot of people, love."

I got Sally up to my apartment on the second floor where, I must admit, she was perfectly at home, with quite a few of her own things there. I told her not to let anyone in. "Even if they say they're cops or whoever."

I had to get geared to what was going on when I got back downstairs. A makeshift interrogation center had been set up in one of the banquet rooms. Hotel guests were trying to provide the police with lists of what had been stolen in the raid, most of it jewelry or cash from the male guests, which was certainly gone with the wind. People's moods varied. Outrage and anger was the loudest note to be heard, but it didn't seem to be aimed at the Beaumont. Free concerts in the park shouldn't be allowed. If they were the city should provide enough police! The Mayor ought to be impeached! Then there were people laughing at each other for the way they looked, clothes torn, faces bruised. Some of the men were happily boasting that they'd gotten in a lick or two on their own. Up in the Trapeze Bar on the mezzanine Eddie, the head bartender, and his staff, in a sea of broken glass and shattered tables and chairs, were serving drinks to the thirsty in paper cups. Mr. Del Greco, the Trapeze's captain, trying to stop the first rush into his domain, had been knocked cold by one of

15

the goons with a baseball bat, and was being tended to up in the hospital unit on the fourth floor—could have a fractured skull, I was told.

I hadn't spotted Chambrun anywhere, and I walked around the mezzanine to his second-floor office. The Man was there, along with Betsy Ruysdale, his secretary, who should have been home and in bed but who is somehow never missing when Chambrun might need her. With them was an old friend, Lieutenant Walter Hardy, a homicide detective with whom we'd had dealings in the past. The Beaumont is a city within a city, with its own bank, shops, restaurants, homes for transients, health club, hospital, its own police force and maintenance crews. Crimes happen here just as they do in other cities, but tonight had been a kind of small war. I hadn't, at that point, heard that anyone had been killed, which would call for a homicide cop. And then, before I asked, I realized that Chambrun had Victoria Haven on his mind.

"There isn't much I can do for you, Pierre," the lieutenant was saying. "No one, at least so far, saw the man who shot at Mrs. Haven. The motive was probably robbery."

"How would he know that Victoria had a small fortune in jewelry up there?" Chambrun asked.

"Rich people live in penthouses," Hardy said. "Just a good guess."

"Why would he try to kill her?" Chambrun asked. "All he had to do was slap her down and go looking for whatever valuables he could find."

"People in that kind of psychotic outburst don't have to make sense," Hardy said. "The time he was up there you figure he could have used an elevator? The power hadn't been turned off yet?"

"I think," Chambrun said. "When this rabble burst into the lobby the help moved to try to stop them. I assume the elevator operators charged out of their cars to try to help the rest of the staff. That probably means nobody saw who took the elevator."

"We've got three bullets from the gun," Hardy said. "Ballistics may be able to tell us if there's a record of some other firing of it. One in a million chances, I'd say. The lady doesn't know of anyone who might be gunning for her?"

"No. She laughs at the idea."

"Well, if ballistics doesn't give us a lead—and I wouldn't hope for it, Pierre—we have no place to start. Possibly, when the smoke has cleared and people have calmed down—and the story breaks in the press and on radio and TV—someone may remember seeing someone commandeer an elevator, or have seen someone coming down the stairways from the roof after the power was shut off. Keep your fingers crossed. It's a chance."

Chambrun moved restlessly from behind his desk. "I have the feeling that someone took advantage of the confusion and went up there to kill Victoria. No connection with the mob at all."

"She'll have to tell you who hates her that much," Hardy said.

Chambrun had his would-be murderer to find, and I had a would-be rapist I wanted to nail to the barn door. But it was mop-up time. The major physical damage to the hotel had taken place in the lobby, the main dining room, the Spartan Room, the Blue Lagoon, and up on the mezzanine in the Trapeze Bar. Of the several hundred thugs who'd invaded the hotel the police had been able to arrest about sixty—the actual number, I find, was sixty-one—and carted them off to jail. The hope was that cooperative guests of the hotel and members of the staff would be able to identify some of them and charge them with specific crimes— armed robbery, unprovoked assault, vandalism.

"Six months in the cooler and they'll be back on the streets again," Mike Maggio said when he passed the word to me that I was wanted to have a look at the prisoners when I could get free. My man wouldn't be hard to identify if they had him. Mr. Cardoza had left him well marked.

I had expected to sit in on the press conference with Chambrun, but he asked me to keep circulating, make contact with the guests who had complaints, possibly with identifications and descriptions. Everybody, it seemed, wanted to talk to someone about their personal experiences during the riot, and express their outrage, mostly against the Mayor and the police force. I don't think I heard one person hold the hotel accountable for what had happened to them.

While all this was going on, still another miracle was happening. Every member of the hotel staff was at work; people on the day shift called back or came back on their own when they heard the news on radio or TV. No one who works for Chambrun will ever let him down, because they know he will never let them down. The cleanup had looked as if it would take a year. Only a little more than an hour after the mob had been hustled out of the hotel, the broken glass and broken furniture were gone, most of it replaced by emergency supplies from the storerooms. The Blue Lagoon was closed for the night, but the Spartan Bar on the lobby level, the lobby itself, and the Trapeze on the mezzanine were doing business, and a stranger who didn't know what had happened wouldn't have noticed anything

18

special—except for the unusual number of blue-uniformed cops filtering in and out.

About three in the morning, it was possible for me to go to police headquarters to have a look at the prisoners who'd been taken. They all looked alike, I thought; blue jeans, gaudy sports shirts, a collection of facial bruises and cuts. I questioned the cops in charge, but they didn't have anyone with a knife wound in the shoulder. Quite a few guests were present, still wearing rather rumpled-looking evening clothes, pointing to this or that prisoner and being jeered at for their pains. It didn't look as if many of the prisoners could be charged with specific crimes, only the mob invasion. That wasn't good enough for me, but what could I do? Go out into a city of millions of people and hope to stumble on a man with a knife wound in his shoulder?

There was a reddish light to the east of the city as I got back to the hotel. "Red in the morning, sailor take warning." It looked as if we were due for a stormy day. I was dead on my feet when I finally made my way up to my apartment on the Beaumont's second floor.

I let myself in with my key and instantly heard Sally call out to me, "Is that you, Mark?"

"I have the only key," I said.

I walked into the bedroom, and there she was, covered with a sheet, and looking very appetizing in spite of her bruised face.

"I thought you'd never come," she said.

"Nobody bothered you?"

"No."

I told her I'd been down to the police station in the hope of identifying the man who'd attacked her. "No luck," I said. "The bastard must have gotten away."

Then the bedside phone rang. I figured Chambrun must

be needing me for something and I wished he didn't. I'd had it. It was Mrs. Veach, the chief operator on the switchboard.

"There's a man trying to reach you, Mark," she said. "He says his name is Max London."

"Never heard of him," I said.

"He says he's Hilary Foster's agent and manager," Mrs. Veach told me. "He says it's urgent."

"Put him through," I said.

The voice that came through was sharp and agitated. "Haskell? I'm Max London, Hilary Foster's manager."

"I've been told," I said.

"Where is she?" London asked.

"I haven't the faintest idea. I saw her a couple of hours ago, but that's it."

"She was all right?"

"Yes. She was taking care of one of the girls who was hurt during what went on here. You know about it?"

"Of course I know. That's why I was worried. She hasn't turned up at her own apartment. Nobody seems to know where she is."

"Why did you happen to call me? Miss Foster isn't a friend of mine. I mean, I just know her to say hello to since she's been working in the Blue Lagoon."

"Because the captain there—what's his name, Cardoza?—said Hilary was taking care of a friend of yours who'd been hurt. That when you arrived, Hilary left. I thought—I hoped—she might have told you where she was going."

"She just said she had to let some friends know that she hadn't been hurt in the ruckus here."

"Didn't say who?"

20

"No. And understand, she wasn't hurt. She was perfectly okay."

I heard a long sigh. "Well, thanks anyway. I'm sorry to have bothered you. And Haskell . . ."

"Yes?"

"She might come back for some reason—curiosity, anything. If she does, please get her to call me."

"Mr. London, I've been going for about twenty hours straight. I'm going to be sound asleep."

"Could you ask someone on the staff there to keep an eye out for her? Most of the hotel help must know her by sight."

"This place is a madhouse just now," I said. "I'll do my best for you."

I did sleep, but before I drifted off I'd gotten Mike Maggio on the phone and asked him to keep an eye out for Hilary Foster.

"She's not around unless she's doubling for one of the cleaning women," Mike told me.

It didn't seem I'd been asleep for more than a few minutes—it was actually a couple of hours—when my phone rang again. Damn Max London, I thought. But I had to answer. It could be something else.

It was something else. "Mr. Chambrun wants you in his office on the double, Mark," Mrs. Veach told me.

I splashed some water on my face, combed my hair, got into some clothes and went down the hall to The Man's office. I wasn't feeling any too cheerful, I don't mind saying, but when I walked into Chambrun's elegant office I thought I'd arrived at a wake.

Chambrun was sitting at his carved Florentine desk, his face the color of ashes. His hand rested on his telephone, like a man trying to remember a forgotten number. Betsy Ruysdale stood beside him, waiting for some kind of instruction that didn't come. Jerry Dodd stood facing Chambrun, like a soldier at attention—or a man facing a firing squad.

Chambrun's thin lips moved. "Play it for him, Ruysdale," he said. He has a way of neutering Betsy by only using her last name. There are rumors that they are a lot closer than that, but you'd never guess it when they are at work.

Betsy moved around the desk. "Mr. Chambrun got a phone call a little while back. We've been flooded with calls from people in trouble and with complaints. But when this conversation started Mr. Chambrun realized there was something odd about it and switched on his tape recorder. Three or four sentences have been spoken when the tape picks it up." She bent down and switched on the recorder.

"Just stop interrupting and listen to what I have to say," a strange voice said. "I am in Suite Twenty-two B. Don't bother to look at your registration cards. I am not Raul Ortiz, who is supposed to be the occupant."

"Who are you?" Chambrun's voice.

"That is of no consequence. Just listen and do what you're told. I have taken over this suite along with several men of mine. We are holding four hostages."

"Who are they?"

"That doesn't matter to you," the voice said—I thought there was a kind of sneering note to it—"except that we have them. I want you to evacuate all the other guests on this corridor. They'll probably be happy enough to leave when you tell them we've taken over this area. You will order the maids who cover this floor to leave. I want no service of any kind to this floor except the telephone. It is to be completely deserted."

"You really think I will follow such instructions?" Chambrun again.

"I will tell you who one of the hostages is," the voice from Twenty-two B said. "She is the star of your nightclub show."

"Hilary Foster?"

"Who else? If you haven't done exactly what I tell you within an hour, the little lady will be dropped out the window. Twenty-two floors to the street below and there shouldn't be very much left of her. Now you're thinking of the police. I advise against telling them what the situation is. If they start to be heroic, send in some kind of SWAT team, the other hostages will go, one by one. I can tell you that you won't be thanked by people in high places if that should happen. If they persist, after they've caused the murder of four important people, I should tell you we have enough high explosives stored here to rip the guts out of your hotel. So you have your orders, Mr. Chambrun. You have one hour in which to get everyone off this floor, stop all services except the phone, and make no effort to get to us unless you want to pay the price. Clear?"

"I will do what I can do," Chambrun said, in a voice I'd never heard before. "I'll call you when I have something to report."

"You will not call me, I will call you," the voice said. "We'll accept no in-calls. I want the phone only for out-calls, long distance in particular."

"An hour isn't much time," Chambrun said. "Thirty or forty people have to be alerted, packed up, moved out."

"An hour is all the time you have. Goodbye, Mr. Chambrun."

The recording was over. The machine made a clicking noise and Betsy Ruysdale turned it off.

My mouth felt dry. "Hilary Foster *is* missing," I said. "Her manager called me a couple of hours ago."

The corner of Chambrun's mouth twitched. "I know. Max London also called me."

"This is a crazy time," I said. "First an invasion by those goons. Then someone takes a shot at Mrs. Haven. Now this."

"You see no connection?" Chambrun asked.

"I'm a little too dizzy to put things together," I said. "What's cooking?"

"We're warning people on the twenty-second floor west that some of the invaders have taken over a suite there. We're moving them out."

"So you're giving in?"

Chambrun brought his fist down hard on the desk. "I'm giving in until I can figure out some way *not* to give in!"

2

How do you not give in with the lives of four hostages hanging in the balance and a suite full of explosives that could blow your hotel to pieces?

"Have you notified the police?" I asked.

"Not yet," Chambrun said, "but the Police Commissioner is on his way to see me about our earlier troubles."

"Who is this Raul Ortiz who's registered in Twenty-two B?" I asked. I should have known. I'd seen his registration card when we'd gone through the regular routine of checking on the new arrivals each morning. Betsy Ruysdale handed me a card off the desk.

RAUL ORTIZ—representing the OAS at the United Nations. "The OAS is what?" I asked.

"Organization of American States," Jerry Dodd told me. "Here to talk about peace in Central America."

"Could he be one of the hostages?" I asked.

"Or our friend on the phone," Chambrun said. "He's been here for about a week. Plenty of time to prepare for something—if he's the one."

"You wouldn't recognize his voice?"

"I never had any reason to talk to Ortiz," Chambrun said.

"If you monitor his phone, you'll know who he's calling and what demands he's making," I said.

25

"He knows I can do just that and it doesn't bother him," Chambrun said. "We'll find out who the other hostages are and that, he must think, will make us even less likely to try something."

"Makes you wonder about the whole night," Jerry Dodd said. "Did that mob charge in here just to rob and raise hell, or were they deliberately here to act as a diversion while the main people took over Twenty-two B and grabbed their hostages?"

"It could be that way," Chambrun said, his dark eyes narrowed in their deep pouches. "And to give someone time to put Victoria Haven out of business. I'm convinced that wasn't just a chance shooting, Jerry."

"The cops took almost sixty prisoners," Jerry said, "almost all of them blacks and Hispanics. Some kind of a 'cause'?"

"Half a million dollars worth of loot in jewels and cash would be cause enough for almost anyone," I said.

Chambrun glanced at me. "Could be just the tip of the iceberg," he said. "Hostages being held to demand a lot more than that." He brought his fist down on the desk again. "So help me . . . !" He didn't finish.

The telephone rang and Betsy Ruysdale answered. She glanced at The Man. "The State Department in Washington," she said.

Chambrun leaned forward and switched on the squawk box on his desk so we could all hear the conversation.

"Pierre Chambrun here."

"Mr. Chambrun, I'm Frank Laughton, calling for the Secretary of State. We've heard about the upheaval at your place last night. We've been trying to reach one of our people who's registered there—Sheldon Tranter. He doesn't answer his room phone."

"We're not expected to nursemaid our guests, Mr. Laughton."

"Quite. But the radio says the people who raided your hotel were mostly blacks and Hispanics. Could be Cubans, Central Americans, we suppose. Tranter is an expert on that area. We wondered—"

"Nobody has behaved quite normally in this hotel since a little before last midnight," Chambrun interrupted. "People changed plans, did things they wouldn't normally do, altered normal time schedules. I'll have to check where your Mr. Tranter is registered—" As he spoke Betsy Ruysdale slipped a card in front of him. Chambrun gave her a wry little smile and went back to the phone. "I see he's in Room 1712. I still don't have a final report on all the areas that were invaded by those thugs last night. But we have checked every floor and every room and that there were no serious injuries to anyone—painful and disfiguring wounds, but not serious."

"Can you take a special look for Tranter?" Laughton asked. "The Secretary would appreciate it, I think I can say that the President would appreciate it."

"Look, Mr. Laughton, there is no rule that says a man has to spend the night in his hotel room. Friends, a romance—"

"In this instance the circumstances are a little different," Laughton said. "Tranter is involved in very delicate negotiations involving national security. He would not, normally, be anywhere we couldn't stay in constant touch with him. I understand what happened there can have upset normal routines, but if Sheldon Tranter is in one piece he should have been in touch with us to let us know just that."

"We'll do what we can to locate him for you," Chambrun said.

"Please call me during the next hour, whether the news is good or bad," Laughton said. He gave Chambrun a Washington number.

Jerry Dodd started for the door. "I'll start the ball rolling," he said. "Someone on the staff must know this Tranter by sight."

"Pass it on to someone else," Chambrun said, "and then get yourself some rest. You've been on the go for almost twenty-four hours."

Jerry grinned at The Man. "You too, Boss," he said.

"An exhausted zombie isn't going to be much use to us," Chambrun said.

When Jerry left, Chambrun leaned back in his desk chair and sat for a moment with the tips of his fingers pressed against what must have been tired eyes. God knows I felt I could use a couple of hours of shut-eye.

Betsy had answered another ring on the phone. "There's a flood of calls for you, Mr. Chambrun," she said. "Press, people with missing friends. The whole world seems to assume that their unaccounted-for friends must have been here last night. Mrs. Veach has to use her own judgment on who to put through."

"I really don't want to take any calls except from Twenty-two B," Chambrun said. "But tell Mrs. Veach I trust her. Let her know I'm expecting the Police Commissioner."

"You're going to tell him?" I asked.

"I don't know—yet," Chambrun said. He straightened up. "I'm concerned about Mrs. Haven, Mark. She's had some time to think about what happened to her. Maybe something has occurred to her that would help. Go to see her, will you, Mark? She'll talk to you. She's fond of you."

"What am I after?" I asked him.

"Some recall of someone who has it in for her," Chambrun said. "By now she must have had a chance to sift through her past and come up with something—if there is something."

"I'll get back to you," I said, and took off.

I went down the stairs from the second floor to the lobby where I could get an elevator to the roof. I've talked about miracles, and what the maintenance people had done with the wrecked lobby was certainly one. Unless you were as familiar with small details as I was, the lobby looked in perfectly normal working order.

I was headed for the bank of elevators when Johnny Thacker, the day bell captain, stopped me.

"Nice to see someone who might be able to tell me what the hell's going on in this palace," Johnny said. He's a nice-looking blond guy, probably in his mid-thirties, who knew the workings of the hotel almost as well as Chambrun himself.

"What are you talking about, Johnny?"

"I'm talking about the twenty-second floor," he said. "All the guests except the South American bunch in suite Twenty-two B have been evacuated, maids taken off duty. Chambrun's orders. Why?"

"You better ask him yourself," I said.

"I would, if Mrs. Veach would put me through to him. What is it, Mark? You have to know. You've been with him for the last hour."

I couldn't tell him, and I'm not a very good liar when I'm talking to people who know me well. "I think the boss has reason to think some of last night's mob may be holed in up there," I said.

"No security people, no cops," Johnny said. "Is that how you deal with crooks?"

"Look," I said, "the police commissioner is on his way. I

29

imagine he'll advise the boss how to handle things. Meanwhile Chambrun's handling it the way he thinks best."

"Tell him he better let some of us know what's cooking." Johnny said. He was angry, and I couldn't blame him. "Everyone on duty's asking questions, and when the next shift comes on they'll be asking. If the boss has something going he better tell us what it is before someone upsets the applecart. You know we'll all go along with whatever he wants, Mark, but we deserve to be told what it is. Tell him that, will you?"

"I'll tell him," I said.

The operator on the roof car asked me the same kind of questions on the way up. "What's going on on Twenty-two?"

Walking out onto the roof, I was conscious for the first time of a gorgeous summer morning. The minute I headed for the middle penthouse, I was closed in on by two of Jerry Dodd's men. I wasn't a stranger to them and they had to know I wasn't a danger to Mrs. Haven. They, too, wanted to know what was cooking on the twenty-second floor. I had to play it dumb.

When I rang the penthouse doorbell I was confronted by Joe Simpson, another of Jerry's boys. He was staying inside with the lady.

"She up and around?" I asked him.

He nodded toward the inside and I could hear a radio or TV set going full blast. "Probably the only person in this dump who isn't exhausted," Simpson said.

"Ask her if she'll see me. The boss wants to reassure himself about her."

Simpson went back into the living room, the radio or TV was turned off, and Victoria Haven called out, "Mark! Come in! Am I glad to see someone from the other world!"

She looked marvelous. She is tall and straight, and just

30

then looked thirty years younger than her actual age. Her dark red hair wasn't natural, I assumed, but it didn't look dyed. She is really something. She was sitting on a sofa in the living room, surrounded by newspapers. A silver coffee pot and several cups were on the low table beside her.

"I've been prepared for a party, but nobody came," she said. She gestured toward the coffee and a plate of cinnamon buns. "I was beginning to think I was forgotten, except for the watchdogs." She patted the sofa beside her. "Come on, Mark. Catch me up on things. The reporters on the radio and TV don't seem to know what the score is."

I sat down beside her. The coffee and buns looked inviting. She poured for me and gestured toward the buns. "Now," she said, "as they used to say in the theater, 'take it from the top,' my friend."

"It's been a crazy time," I said. "The lobby, the bars, wrecked. Some of those goons sifting up into the hotel, robbing people in their rooms. But you? You're okay? You're not hurting?"

She was wearing a pale blue chiffon robe with long sleeves. If you didn't know she'd been wounded you'd have had no way of guessing it.

"I got lucky," she said. "Like a pinprick. Pierre?"

"Okay, but pretty well pooped out, like most of us."

"Not hurt? Those monsters didn't get to him?"

"Not hurt," I said, "but worried about you."

"Nothing to worry about," she said. "Whatever it was, it's over. Houdini couldn't get to me now, with Jerry Dodd's men out there."

"What's bothering Chambrun is why somebody tried in the first place."

"Somebody gossiped about what I have up here. Seemed like a way for someone to get rich quick," she said.

"Trying to kill you doesn't make sense when what he had

on his mind was robbery," I said. "All he had to do was shove you in a closet, lock the door, and take all night to find what he wanted."

Putting her coffee cup down in its saucer made a little clicking sound. "I've come to an unfortunate conclusion about that," the lady said. "It had to be someone I knew, at least knew by sight. There was no way he could just push me around to get what he wanted, because I could have put a name to him."

"A hotel employee?"

She gave me a quick little smile. "Pierre wouldn't like to hear me say that. He likes to believe that the people who work for him can be trusted right down to the end of the line. But I'm sure there's been gossip about me, my eccentricities—" She waved a hand around the room. "—this apparent junk pile I live in. The temptation was too great, and when an opportunity arose, when everyone's attention was distracted by those invading vandals, he took it. Took it and failed."

"He missed by an inch, and then you were too quick for him," I said.

She laughed. "You'd think I'd been dodging bullets all my life."

"Have you ever dodged one before?"

She took a sip of her coffee. "Not literally," she said. "In the slang sense—'dodging the bullet,' meaning to escape an accident, a disaster—many times." She chuckled. "Escaping the wrong man quite a few times. And once, long ago, escaping what might have been a violent death. It's odd, Mark, but I was thinking about that one time when you arrived. The radio has been saying over and over that most of the mob that invaded the Beaumont were blacks or Hispanics. My one violent adventure had what you might call Hispanic overtones."

"Tell me." The coffee tasted wonderful, the buns were delicious. I was willing to listen forever.

"It was long ago—forty-five years ago. You weren't even born, Mark. But I—I was thirty-nine and telling myself that I was staring old age in the face. My fortieth birthday was just around the corner! I would spend the rest of my life crocheting place mats, or rolling bandages for the Red Cross." She glanced at me, her eyes twinkling. "I didn't dream how much romantic fun was still to come in my life. I wasn't bad-looking, you know."

"You were beautiful—and still are," I said.

"Flattery will get you almost anything," she said. "But at forty—the approach of old age, I thought—a young man came into my life. He was only thirty, from Central America—Guatemala, to be exact—dark, dashing, a Spanish-style nobleman. Rich, anyway, with what he described as a magnificent estate in his own country. He wasn't playing games with me. He wanted marriage. But first I must go with him to his home country to meet his parents. They must approve, or he might be cut off from what he told me was a huge fortune." She looked away and there was a kind of dreamy look in her still-bright blue eyes. "I wasn't sure I wanted to marry him but, being 'so old,' it might be my last chance for anything permanent. Going to a part of the world I'd never seen was tempting. I could always say no when it came down to having to decide."

"So you went with him to meet his family?"

She nodded. "We didn't fly in those days. My friend had his own private yacht. There were days of cruising south in magnificent weather. I managed to stay pure, you might say, in spite of passionate advances by my young man. We finally arrived at his family estate, somewhere outside Guatemala City. You wouldn't believe it, Mark. It was a castle, a palace—luxury beyond belief: servants, Rolls-

Royces, Arabian saddle horses, and a father and mother who were elegant, cultivated, educated beyond my dreams, who lived like reigning monarchs. They treated me a little like some theatrical floozy their son had lost his head over. There was, I think, a local princess they had ticketed for him.

"They didn't have much time to get to know me," Mrs. Haven went on. "That first night I was in their palace I was abducted."

"You're kidding!"

"Their palace was attacked by an army of guerrillas. I guess things weren't very different down there then than they are now. First one side in power, and then the other. The place was attacked, fires set, gunshots all over the place. I was literally torn out of my bed, and carried away on the pommel of the saddle of a wild-riding horseman who took me up into the mountains. I spoke very little Spanish and the people who took me spoke very little English. I didn't know what it was all about for a day or two. I was held in an elaborate mountain camp, well treated, well fed, but not able to take a step without being confronted by an armed guerrilla. About the fourth day an older man came on the scene—a man in his sixties, I guessed—who spoke English fluently. He told me his name was Carlos Avila. He explained to me that my young man's family, part of the ruling powers at that time, had taken several guerrilla leaders prisoner. He regretted to inform me that I was being held hostage—my life in exchange for the freedom of those guerrilla prisoners. I didn't feel very cheerful about that, Mark. My young man and his parents might regret what had happened to me, but if it meant the loss of a political advantage, to hell with me, I thought. I said as much to that man Avila. He explained to me that my young man's parents were supported by the United States government. The President would bring pressure to bear on them when he knew an American woman's life was in the balance." Her laugh was humorless. "I didn't have much hope that the President would give a damn what happened to me.

"Days went by, and then this Carlos Avilla came to my tent one morning, all smiles. The deal had been made. His guerrilla friends had been set free, and I was to be escorted down to the coast where a cruise ship would take me back to New York. I asked him about my young man and his parents. He gave me a grim smile. 'They have been dealt with,' he told me. He escorted me to a group of horsemen who were to take me down to my ship." She laughed. "That's when I made perhaps the only romantically heroic remarks of a long life, Mark. I looked Mr. Avilla in the eye and said, 'If you ever see me again, remember to kill me, or I will surely see to it that you pay for this.' He just laughed and watched me ride off with his men. There was a government agent waiting for me at the cruise ship. He asked me a hundred questions I couldn't answer. I couldn't identify anyone but Carlos Avilla. I couldn't report any conversations because I didn't speak Spanish well enough. The agent didn't seem to be interested in Avilla, or he already knew all there was to know about him. Later I heard that he ruled the country down there for a while. My young man and his elegant parents were said to have faced a firing squad."

I found myself sitting up straight. "Are you suggesting that your Señor Avilla took your advice—'Remember to kill me'—and was up here on the roof last night?"

She laughed. "You're not thinking, Mark. All that was forty-five years ago. Avilla would be well over a hundred years old, and he couldn't have been here unless he flew down from Heaven or rose up from Hell. It all came back simply because the two violent adventures in my life seem to involve Spanish-speaking people."

I stood up. "Well, so much for that," I said. "I'd better get back to the boss and let him know you're very much alive."

"Tell Pierre to let someone else carry the ball for a while," she said. "He must be dead on his feet."

3

I don't know how long a man can go under a full head of steam without having any rest, but I guess I was about to find out. When I got back to Chambrun's office he was there with Betsy Ruysdale and a stranger who was introduced as "Mr. Guardino, the police commissioner's assistant." It seems the commissioner had been summoned to the mayor's office to explain how things could have gotten so out of hand after the concert in the park.

What I noticed at once was that Chambrun had found time, while I was away, to shave and change his clothes in the private dressing room he had off the office. He looked as fresh as he did on any morning of his life, and I knew for certain that he'd been on the go for better than twenty-four hours.

I waited to make some sort of guess on how much The Man had told Guardino. Had he opened the can of peas represented by the situation in Twenty-two B? Apparently not.

"We think we have a rather special problem on our hands," Guardino explained to me. He'd obviously already been into it with Chambrun. "We don't think this attack on the Beaumont was connected with the concert in the park, but we're going to have to prove it to satisfy the mayor." Guardino was a dark, bright-eyed youngish man—mid-thirties—plenty of energy.

"They came as the concert broke up," I said.

"I know. But we had nearly eleven hundred cops in the park, watching for just this kind of thing. There was no sign of any violence there, no one attacked or robbed. We were congratulating ourselves on having handled everything perfectly there when all hell broke loose here. We think it was well planned in advance, and these goons were waiting somewhere else to hit the hotel, waiting for the right time so it would seem it was another explosion from the park."

"But you don't think it came from there?"

"We're positive it didn't," Guardino said. "From all accounts so far, there were at least two hundred of them— maybe three hundred—moving together. They couldn't have come unnoticed from the park. They struck at just the right time to create this uncertainty, confusion."

"Well, I guess we were an ideal target," I said. "Rich people's home away from home."

"Quite so," Guardino said. "We have now taken sixty-one prisoners. Some of them have police records that suggest that this mob was made up of terrorists representing communist revolutionaries in Central America—anti-American. Whether they just chose a lush spot to raise money, or whether they were after some of the diplomatic personnel who stay here at the hotel, we don't know yet."

I glanced at Chambrun. His face was an expressionless mask. He had the answer to Guardino's question, located on the twenty-second floor of his hotel. He had been warned that if he told the police what the situation was, the four hostages the guy in Twenty-two B claimed to have would be dropped out the window, one by one.

"So far we have had only one inquiry about someone who might be involved," Guardino said. "The State Department has asked us to find one of their men who's staying here; a man named Sheldon Tranter. He's an expert on the Central American situation. Mr. Chambrun tells me that Washington has asked you about Tranter, too."

"I also told you that Jerry Dodd, my security chief, is trying to track Tranter down," Chambrun said, in a flat, colorless voice. "The fact that he isn't in his room doesn't necessarily mean anything. He could have spent the night with friends, here in the city, somewhere in the suburbs. He couldn't guess anyone could be concerned about him until he reads the morning paper or hears the news on the radio or the TV. When that happens he'll be in touch with the department."

I knew he could also be one of the hostages in Twenty-two B.

"It's a little too much of a coincidence that an expert on Central America should turn up missing when Central American terrorists are involved," Guardino said.

He was right, of course.

"I hope it is a coincidence," Chambrun said.

"Anyone else missing?" Guardino asked.

Max London would have spread the word about Hilary Foster, and it would get back to Guardino sooner or later.

"Hilary Foster, who is starring in our nightclub, has turned up among the unaccounted for," Chambrun said. "Her manager has been asking for her. She was performing when the invasion began. She stayed behind to help one of the girls who'd been hurt. Haskell, here, saw her and talked to her."

"She was fine, not hurt," I said. "She said she was taking off to let friends know that she was okay."

"Probably stayed with those friends," Chambrun said. "Not surprising if she was suffering from shock, and needed comfort. Hasn't thought to call everyone who might be concerned for her."

It was said so casually. Hilary, he knew, was on the twenty-second floor.

Guardino got up from the chair he'd been occupying. "The Commissioner will be in touch if there's anything new," he said. "If this man Tranter—and the Foster girl—show up, you might let us know." He stood there, frowning at us. "I find it hard to believe this was all just a case of robbery and vandalism? Something political—a threat, a warning? I'll feel better when Sheldon Tranter shows up. He could be in big trouble."

"Aren't we all?" Chambrun said. He made it sound as though he was thinking about property damage.

As soon as Chambrun and I and Betsy Ruysdale were alone, he asked me about Mrs. Haven.

"You'd never know anything had happened to her if you weren't told," I said.

"She able to recall anything that might help?"

I laughed. "An abduction forty-five years ago," I said, and told him her story of her Central American adventure.

Chambrun sat very still, staring at the Picasso painting on the far wall. " 'Remember to kill me'," he said, almost to himself. "There *is* a connection—Central America."

"Not very real," I said. "This Avilla character was in his sixties forty-five years ago. You visualize a guy over a hundred years old running around on the roof taking potshots at an ancient lady?"

"Nor do I buy coincidences," Chambrun said.

The phone rang and Betsy answered it. "Mrs. Veach," she said. "Urgent."

Chambrun switched on the squawk box again and Mrs. Veach was audible to all of us. "Room Twenty-two B is making a long-distance call to a number in London, England," our chief operator told us.

"Splice us in," Chambrun said.

We could hear the long-distance operator reporting. "I have Lord Huntingdon for you."

"Huntingdon here," a very British voice said. "Who is this calling?"

Then the voice we knew from earlier took over. "Who I am doesn't matter, Huntingdon. Just listen because I will only say it once. I'm in the Beaumont Hotel in New York City. It's possible you've already heard what's happened here during the night. I have taken some hostages here in the hotel, and one of them is Sir George Brooks."

The British voice was calm. "Have you harmed him?"

"Not yet, but I promise you he will be very dead if you don't do exactly what I tell you."

"I'm listening," Huntingdon said.

"Your government will use its influence to procure the release of revolutionary prisoners who are being held in Guatemala. There are eight of them. You know their names. They will be set safely free within the next twenty-four hours or Brooks will pay for your failure to act with his life."

"You are surely aware that Her Majesty's government is not in a position to act alone in this matter," the cool British voice said.

"I know. The government of the United States is involved, and the Organization of American States. We have hostages that will help persuade them, too. They are about to be informed of that fact. You have just twenty-four hours to comply—or else."

"You're not giving us enough time," Huntingdon said.

"It's all the time I've got to give," the man in Twenty-two B said. "I will not be calling you again. I cannot be bargained with, Huntingdon."

There was a clicking sound and we knew our friend from Twenty-two B had hung up.

"Hello! Hello! Are you still there?" For the first time Huntingdon sounded concerned.

"Your party has disconnected," the operator said.

"Damn!" Huntingdon said, and was gone. He'd obviously be calling back.

"What will you tell him?" I asked Chambrun.

"It depends on what he tells me," Chambrun said.

"The cat's out of the bag," I said. "You'll have Mrs. Thatcher demanding that you do something."

"Or demanding that I do nothing!" Chambrun said. "That madman's next call will be to the State Department to inform them that he has their man Tranter. And then the OAS to let them know that he has their man Raul Ortiz, our guest in Twenty-two B."

"They will be telling you what they want done," I said.

Chambrun gave me his hanging-judge look. "You forget we've been warned of explosives that could rip the hotel apart," he said. "I'll do what I think best, no matter what kings and queens and ambassadors have to suggest."

"I don't understand about Sir George Brooks," Betsy Ruysdale said. "He was there on the roof after Mrs. Haven was shot, and from then on there was no way anyone could have got to him up there."

"Nothing to stop him from going down into the hotel to see what was going on," Chambrun said. He reached for the cup of Turkish coffee which Betsy always kept hot on his desk. "'Remember to kill me,'" he muttered. "Only Victoria could dream up such a line!"

The phone rang. It was Mrs. Veach to tell us that Twenty-two B was calling a number in Washington.

"Here we go again," Chambrun said. He glanced at his watch. "We have until this time tomorrow—ten-thirty A.M."

We live in a world that poses a constant threat of violence, and yet we don't pay very much attention to it. We have been told over and over that Russia and the United States have enough nuclear weapons to destroy each other ten times over. But it surely won't happen, will it? The President tells us that naval maneuvers off Central America have been standard practice for years. Nothing to worry about. Yet revolutionary forces in that part of the world are armed and supported by Communist Russia. Somebody pulls a nuclear trigger and our world could be blown to pieces. But it won't happen, will it? Not to us—not to me! We are told our hotel is threatened with destruction, but it won't happen, will it. Or will it? The streets of our city are filled with thugs who could attack you, rob you, beat you. Yet I walk those streets every day, certain that nothing like that could ever happen to me. But could it? The safest place in my world was this hotel where I live and work, run like a Swiss watch, guarded by professionals, and yet, now, it had been turned upside down. What couldn't possibly happen to us had happened to us. Twenty-four hours and then . . .

One thing was certain now. We were going to have a second invasion, this time by representatives of governments and political groups. The police would be coming back in force, probably the FBI, the CIA, and God knew who else. Chambrun was going to have to admit that he, too, had been threatened by the hostage-takers and given into them for the time being. Ten to one he was going to lose control of his own precious world.

He seemed immobilized by the prospect. I expected to see him in action, but instead he just sat there in his office, staring at the wall opposite his desk. He was wrestling, I thought, with possible courses of action to take, and finding none that would work.

I had thought of a swarm of people coming our way but it didn't happen quite like that. Jerry Dodd appeared, and with him a stranger—a tall man with red hair and very cold blue eyes, a little red mustache shading a tight slit of a mouth.

"I'm sorry to break in, Boss, but Mr. Yardley didn't give me any choice," Jerry said.

Yardley stepped forward and put down a small wallet on Chambrun's desk. "My credentials, Mr. Chambrun," he said. His voice was cold and colorless.

Chambrun looked at the wallet and handed it back. "CIA," he said. He seemed to make an effort to pull himself together. "This is Mark Haskell, my public relations man, and Miss Ruysdale, my private secretary."

Yardley gave us a curt nod. "I'm stationed in New York," he said. "Half an hour ago I got a call from my chief in Washington telling me what was going on here."

"It's not a secret," Chambrun said. "It's been all over the radio, the TV, the newspapers. We had a sizeable riot."

"I'm not talking about what everyone knows, Chambrun. I'm talking about what you know. Frank Laughton of the State Department got a call from someone who is holding hostages. He managed to trace the call and it came from here in your hotel, through your switchboard. Are the hostages being held here?"

Chambrun hesitated. He didn't really have any choice.

"Mr. Laughton isn't the only person who got a call from here," Chambrun said.

"I know. British security got on to Laughton before he talked to me."

"And you came alone?" Chambrun asked.

"To find out what the situation is before we act," Yardley said. "I assume you can tell us, and without any stalling, Mr. Chambrun. This isn't just some kind of hoodlum kidnapping. It's far bigger and more sensitive than that."

"So I have guessed," Chambrun said. He had to lay it on the table. He gave it to Yardley without holding anything back, the raid on the hotel, the attack on Victoria Haven, the involvement of Sir George Brooks, and then the phone call from Twenty-two B informing him of the hostage-taking and the demand that Twenty-two West be cleared of guests.

"And you gave up without a murmur?" Yardley asked.

"What would you have done, Mr. Yardley? They claimed they had four hostages, one of them the star of our nightclub show. They claimed to have explosives enough to blow my hotel to pieces. My security force was in disarray as a result of the raid. The demand to clear the floor of guests was all he asked of me. I needed time to figure a way to handle it."

"You didn't tell the police?"

"I needed time, damn it! I didn't want an army barging in here and find myself watching bodies go by my window there on the way to the sidewalk!"

Yardley seemed to relax. "Let's start over," he said. "I think you did what you had to do. You have any idea what they really want?"

"I listened in on their phone call to Lord Huntingdon in London," Chambrun said. "And on the call to Laughton in Washington. Political prisoners must be released."

"We know from those calls who two of the hostages are," Yardley said. "Sheldon Tranter, one of our people, and Sir George Brooks, the Britisher. You mentioned a girl entertainer. Is she Hispanic?"

"No. I think they took her to bring special pressure on me," Chambrun said.

"And the fourth hostage?"

"It's a guess. I think it is Raul Ortiz, who is registered in Twenty-two B. He's a member of the Organization of American States."

"But no phone call to his people?"

"Probably not necessary," Chambrun said. "Or the call made from somewhere else, by someone else."

"Our problem is to coordinate our efforts," Yardley said. "We don't want the police trying one approach, the British trying another, our people trying still another, Central American people trying still another, and you trying to save your hotel and your girl singer."

"I'd like to think you know that I'm concerned with all four hostages," Chambrun said. "I want to see all of them safe and my hotel in one piece. I wish I could be as sure of you and the others."

"Meaning?"

"Meaning that what's at stake for you isn't nearly as clear as what's at stake for me," Chambrun said. "I want to save four lives—and possibly many more if we get down to setting off explosives. But what are the value of those lives as against freedom for eight political prisoners? Would freeing those prisoners be a political defeat of consequence? Would failure to free them lead to a confrontation with an enemy, backed by Russian arms and technology? After the four hostages in Twenty-two B are dead I can hear piously expressed regrets of people in high places. After all, we couldn't knuckle under to terror tactics, could we? The loss of four lives and the gutting of a hotel is tragic, but setting free those eight prisoners could have cost us thousands of lives in a war! It's all right for us to hold hostages—because that's what those eight prisoners are—but it's monstrous for the enemy to hold hostages, but we have to consider what giving into them might cost."

"Something like that," Yardley said very quietly.

"I am in charge of a little city of my own," Chambrun said. "I am concerned with my people, my guests who are under my protection, my property. Your big-time operators and their covert ball games don't concern me, Mr. Yardley."

"But you can't prevent it if the decision is to move in on you with a large force of men," Yardley said.

"I can give it one hell of a try," Chambrun said.

For the first time Yardley seemed to become something like human. He took a pack of cigarettes from his pocket, lit the cigarette he took from it with a lighter, and sat down on the arm of the chair next to Chambrun's desk. He smiled, and it was friendly, not threatening.

"I find myself deciding that you're my kind of guy, Mr. Chambrun," he said. "You didn't ask for this mess but you're not backing away from it. I wonder if we can talk to each other—off the record?"

"Unless I need to use what you tell me to save those hostages and my hotel," Chambrun said.

"Fair enough," Yardley said. He glanced at me and then

at Betsy Ruysdale, who was standing behind Chambrun's chair, and then at Jerry Dodd, who hadn't spoken a word.

"My right arm and my left arm," Chambrun said, "and my chief of staff. No secrets from them, but silence if I ask for it."

"Fair enough," Yardley said. He took a deep drag on his cigarette and let the smoke out in a long sigh. "I can't decide the tactics my people will use. I can only advise. I can't promise you anything because I haven't got the power to deliver. But I can certainly urge my people to consult with you before they move on their own. When you invade a strange country, you need help from people who know the terrain. Your hotel is a strange country to us. We need your help. According to the man on the phone, we now have a little less than twenty-four hours in which to decide to give in or to attack."

"At the cost of at least four lives and a massive destruction of property."

"Can we discuss the terrain up there on the Twenty-second floor?" Yardley asked.

"There's nothing secret about it," Chambrun said. "The hotel is divided into east and west corridors, divided by banks of elevators that go from the basement to the forty-first floor. There are only two elevators that go all the way to the roof, one in the west bank, and one at the rear in the service area."

"How many elevators go to Twenty-two?"

"Six in the west bank and two in the service area—freight elevators."

"The suite itself—Twenty-two B?"

"A sitting room, two bedrooms, two baths, and a kitchenette. Closets, of course—a pantry in the kitchen. A television set, a radio, telephones in each room. Not in the bathrooms, of course."

"Entrances and exits?"

"Two. One into the main hall, one at the rear into the service area."

"Two ways to approach it, then?"

"Fire stairs, both front and back," Jerry Dodd said, speaking for the first time.

"Actually you can come and go, front or back?"

"Technically, yes," Chambrun said. "Actually, guests aren't expected to use the service area or its facilities."

"But they could?"

"Of course."

"If you're thinking of people coming or going to Twenty-two B the way things are now, no way," Jerry Dodd said. "Elevators won't stop at Twenty-two, and we have the fire stairs, front and back, guarded by security people. No one can sneak up to Twenty-two B, or sneak out."

"Suppose someone took an elevator up and pulled a gun on the operator?" Yardley asked. "He'd stop at Twenty-two, wouldn't he?"

"Sure," Jerry said. "But he'd also have stepped on an emergency button in the floor of the car, right by his controls."

"Which would result in . . . ?"

"Getting him help," Jerry said.

"Shutting off the power in that particular elevator in a matter of seconds," Chambrun said. "At any rate, that hasn't happened. Jerry and I would know."

"Since we got the other guests off that floor, no one has come out of there, or gone up," Jerry said.

Yardley crushed out his cigarette in the ashtray on Chambrun's desk and lit a fresh one. "Suppose we gave in to their demands and released their political prisoners in Guatemala, how do they get out?"

"By releasing their hostages and giving us time to make

sure there are no armed bombs left behind," Chambrun said. "I will personally escort them to the front door when I know the hostages and the hotel are safe."

"Where the police, the FBI, the CIA, the agents of foreign countries will be waiting for them," Yardley said. "They'll know that."

"I suspect they will have demanded free passage," Chambrun said. "If you have given in on their primary demand, you will probably have given in on whatever their plan is to get away."

"And if the powers involved don't give in?"

"I've spent the last two hours, Mr. Yardley, trying to come up with an answer to that question," Chambrun said.

"We're dealing with fanatics," Jerry Dodd said. "They're prepared to be heroes in the eyes of their own people. They will be heroes if they manage to free their comrades in prison, and they will be heroes if they die in the attempt. As far as they're concerned it's 'heads I win, tails you lose.' "

"With death and violence the message they leave behind them if they lose," Chambrun said. "What do you think the people in their White Houses and their palaces will do if we can get that message across to them, Mr. Yardley?"

Yardley's smile was grim. "If I could answer that kind of question, Chambrun, I might be living in a White House myself!"

There were so many things we didn't know. Beside the four hostages, how many people were holed up in Twenty-two B? With no room service, they'd be pretty damned hungry in twenty-four hours, Yardley suggested. Chambrun pointed out that nobody starves to death in twenty-four hours, and how long had they been preparing for this?

There could be enough food in the kitchenette's refrigerator to last them for weeks. We could shut off the water and there would still be enough in the toilet tanks to last them their twenty-four hours. Yardley suggested shutting off the electricity.

"In every suite and guest room in this hotel there is an emergency light, like they have in theaters, battery-powered in case Con Ed does us dirt," Jerry Dodd said.

"Making them uncomfortable isn't going to get us anywhere," Chambrun said. "Would-be heroes can stand quite a little discomfort to earn their medals."

"I think you're both overlooking the most likely situation we'll have to face," Jerry Dodd said.

"Let's have it, Jerry," Chambrun said.

"The British government, and our government, and the OAS people agree to release the eight prisoners they're holding. But heroes or not, these characters who are holding the hostages in Twenty-two B intend to get out of this alive. They're not going to turn over their hostages to you, Boss, and let you escort them out of the hotel to where the cops are waiting. They're not going to release the Foster girl, and Sir George Brooks, and Tranter, and Ortiz until they're safe. And I find myself wondering if you let them take the hostages away somewhere—spirit them out of the hotel through the basement garage in cars we give them to use—will they let them go once they're away?"

"Why not? If their people are free, why would they want to hang onto our people? A deal is a deal."

"Not with those creeps," Jerry said. His face was a dark, angry cloud. "Once they're out of the hotel, they're not safe if they turn the hostages loose. The hostages can identify them, name them probably. Your people, Yardley, and the British and the OAS won't give up until they have these guys nailed to the barn door. The only way they'll be safe is if they silence those hostages forever."

Yardley spoke after a moment of uneasy silence. "You're suggesting they won't deal for prisoners?"

Jerry's smile was a twisted fake. "I wouldn't if I was in their shoes," he said.

"So heads they win and tails we lose," Chambrun said, repeating Jerry's earlier crack.

"That's the way it appears to me," Jerry said. "And it must look that way in the oval office and in Ten Downing Street in London. You give in, release the prisoners you're holding in order to save the hostages in Twenty-two B, and in the end you haven't saved them and you've set eight dangerous men free, ready to attack you from somewhere else. So they'll try to look decent and humane to the people who read the papers and listen to the radio and TV. They'll make it look as if they've tried to make a deal to save those four people upstairs. But, privately, they know they can't save them and so they won't let their prisoners go. They'll have convinced themselves that national securities are at stake."

"You agree with that, Yardley—off the record?" Chambrun asked.

"It's possible," Yardley said. "A tragic possibility, but a possibility."

"Which leaves us where?" I asked.

"It leaves us with a need to find a way to save the hostages in Twenty-two B without any help from the Great White Father in Washington, and the Great White Mother in London," Chambrun said.

"And how do we do that?" I asked.

Chambrun glanced at his wristwatch. "We have about twenty-two hours to come up with that answer," he said.

The music goes round and round and comes out on the same sour note. You agree to terms and your four people come out dead; you attack the suite with a force of men and they still come out dead, plus the possibility that the whole midsection of the hotel is destroyed, the attack force killed along with the kidnappers. You can't decide with the toss of a coin, because whatever way it comes up you lose.

"So there is no way to win," Betsy Ruysdale said, in a voice I scarcely recognized.

Yardley nodded like a man dreaming. "We give in and we lose the four hostages while setting eight dangerous enemies free. We play it tough and we have the eight prisoners but we still lose the four hostages plus no one knows how many more dead, maimed, and wounded as the result of a bombing."

"It isn't much of a choice unless you like the taste of blood," Chambrun said. I don't think I've ever heard him so bitter or so angry.

The red light on the phone blinked and Betsy answered it. She looked at Chambrun and pointed toward the ceiling. Twenty-two B was calling us again. The squawk box was on.

"Chambrun here."

"Time is wasting, Chambrun," the voice said. "Has Yardley persuaded you that you don't have any choice?"

"He's not in a position to persuade me of anything," Chambrun said.

"You must be toying with a dozen choices," the voice said.

"How can we be sure our hostages will be safe if we set your people free?" Chambrun asked.

The man in Twenty-two B chuckled. "You have to trust me."

53

"I'm not in a mood for jokes," Chambrun said.

"I understand. It's not a joking matter, is it? I think we hold the trump cards, Chambrun. We have four hostages who can be dead in a matter of seconds. We can put your hotel out of business for the foreseeable future simply by pressing a button."

"At the cost of your own life," Chambrun said.

"Quite so," the voice said, hardening. "That will give the man who takes my place an extra card to play. The President and the Prime Minister and the OAS people will know that we're not bluffing. There will be more important hostages the next time and damage to more important property than your fancy hotel. All the nuclear bombs and missiles in the world are not going to stop us, Mr. Chambrun. You'd better be persuaded—and persuade the others—to play the game while the stakes are relatively low."

"And if they decide to take your eight revolutionaries out and face them with a firing squad?"

"Then probably three times as many important people on your side will not be eating breakfast tomorrow morning, Mr. Chambrun. Think about it. I'll be back to you in a couple of hours. I suggest you bear one thing in mind. We have considered all the alternatives and we know exactly what we will do, whatever you decide."

The phone clicked off.

"Checkmate," Yardley said in a flat voice.

Chambrun's hand wasn't quite steady as he reached for the cup of Turkish coffee on his desk. "I have never known any man who, in a crisis, didn't overlook something," he said.

"What have they overlooked?" Yardley said.

"I was talking about me, Mr. Yardley," Chambrun said. "What have *I* overlooked?"

I suppose you can live next door to a man, work for him, and not respect him; even hold him in contempt. I lived, you might say, "next door" to Chambrun, spent most of every working day of my life with him and I not only had respect for him, I could say I idolized him—like a kid feels about a loving father. That day, in spite of the dark picture they'd managed to paint, I didn't really believe Chambrun wouldn't come up with an answer.

Sam Yardley had contacted us about an hour ago and I thought his attitude then was slightly hostile. He was CIA, a professional in the world of terrorism and violence. Chambrun, and Jerry Dodd and the rest of us just hotel people. We could tell him where the men's room was, where a power switch was, and we could monitor phone calls in and out—though it would be better if one of his own people was doing the monitoring. After an hour with Chambrun in his office Yardley, I think, had become a friend. Chambrun had earned his respect and confidence. But was he expecting too much of Chambrun? Was I?

Something I hadn't anticipated happened shortly after the man in Twenty-two B hung up on the boss. Johnny Thacker, the day bell captain, appeared at the office door carrying an armful of newspapers.

"You haven't wanted to tell us what's cooking here, Mr. Chambrun," Johnny said, "but all we have to do is read the extra editions of the newspapers and listen to the radio and TV." He put the papers down on Chambrun's desk.

It was all there, the story of last night's raid, the names of the hostages, the demands made by the people holding them. We hadn't released anything to reporters. The information had to have come from the kidnappers. How had they gotten it out? Every phone call out from Twenty-two B had been listened to by Mrs. Veach and her people at the switchboard. There'd been nothing from there that accounted for this. No one but the guests being evacuated had left the twenty-second floor.

"Is there a reporter you trust, Mark, circulating downstairs?" Chambrun asked me.

"Jack Wilson, International News," I said.

"You know him by sight, Johnny?" Chambrun asked Thacker.

"No problem," Johnny said. "There's an army of reporters waiting at the lobby stairs, waiting to get up to you."

"Just Wilson. Get him up here on the double. And Johnny—"

Johnny hesitated at the door.

"I'm sorry to have kept you in the dark so long. We've been trying to develop a plan of action. So far, nothing that makes sense."

Johnny managed a smile. "We trust you, Boss. Although we've been itching real bad!"

"I can understand and I'm sorry. We hadn't expected this." Chambrun tapped the stack of newspapers. "I want all the heads of departments here in my office in half an hour—you, get Mike Maggio back here—"

"He never left," Johnny said.

"Mr. Atterbury from the front desk. McIntosh from engineering, Mrs. Veach from the switchboard, Jack Borglum, maintenance. Anyone who runs any department."

"Front desk may be a problem," Johnny said. "Guests are

lined up like cordwood trying to check out before we get blown into the East River. Rats deserting the sinking ship."

"Wouldn't you leave if you thought a bomb was about to go off?" Chambrun said.

Johnny managed a grin. "Not till you told me to, Boss. So tell me in time, will you?" He took off.

Yardley was scowling at one of the newspapers as he read it. "There's almost more here than I know," he said. "Details of the demands made to London and Washington, names of the hostages. That includes Raul Ortiz—we were only guessing about him—Hilary Foster, Sheldon Tranter, Sir George Brooks. The threat to blow up the hotel and put you out of business for a long time and kill or hurt God knows how many others. The reporters have been told every damn thing there is to know!"

"I shouldn't be surprised," Chambrun said. "The man upstairs knew you were here, talking to me, Yardley."

"That bothered me, too," Yardley said. "How could he know that? There've been no calls in to Twenty-two B. Nobody could have told them I was here."

"But somebody did," Chambrun said. "I wouldn't expect a man in your job to be surprised, Yardley. You people mess around with all the modern technologies. Some kind of sophisticated walkie-talkie radio that bypasses us? None of what's happened is spur of the moment. They can have been preparing for a long time."

"The concert in the park."

"Just helped them set a date—a time to set their goons loose. I think we have to face an unpleasant fact. There's someone ambling around the hotel whom we have no reason to suspect—a guest, a regular patron of one of our bars—who had all this information in advance, who can watch every move we make, and has means to communicate with Twenty-two B."

"So we look for a guy who's carrying some kind of radio," Jerry Dodd said.

"Don't be foolish, Jerry. He won't be carrying anything that could incriminate him. He watches, sees what's important, and goes to his radio in an apartment down the block, or another hotel around the corner."

"Could be someone on your staff," Yardley said.

"I'd bet my life against that," Chambrun said.

"These people have access to staggering sums of money," Yardley said. "Enough to turn an honest man's conscience into mush."

Chambrun's face was grim. "If that should be true, if someone I trust has sold us out, I'll go up to Twenty-two B and take the first dive out the window," he said.

"You trust your people that much?" Yardley asked.

"That much," Chambrun said.

Johnny Thacker came back with Jack Wilson, the IN reporter. Johnny must have been right. The reporters were just down the hall at the foot of the mezzanine stairs. Wilson is a sort of young Jack Lemmon type, with a sardonic smile that suggests he finds all the horrors he covers faintly amusing.

"To what do I owe the honor of being chosen from the common herd?" he asked. "The boys and girls downstairs will eat me alive when I go back."

"Mark trusts you," Chambrun said. "I need one set of clear answers and not a thousand questions. Are you willing? If not, we'll pick someone else."

"I'll answer what I can," Wilson said, "if you'll answer one question for me."

"Which is?"

"Do you have a plan of action?"

"No," Chambrun said.

Wilson's eyebrows lifted slightly. "You don't believe they'll do what they threaten to do?"

"I believe they'll do what they threaten to do, and more," Chambrun said.

"And you have no plan?"

"That's three questions, Mr. Wilson. Now it's my turn," Chambrun said. He touched the newspapers on his desk. "I haven't read your story, but I suspect they're all pretty much the same. Where did the information you have come from?"

"The telephone," Wilson said.

"You took the call?"

"No. It came to our managing editor's desk. I was already here. The news of the raid on the hotel had already come in and I got the assignment to cover it."

"So what you know is secondhand?"

"Yes and no," Wilson said. "My boss taped the call when it came in. The caller laid it on the line—hostages, bomb, the works. He told us London and Washington had been informed. He told us you had complied with his first demand, clearing everyone off the twenty-second floor. He told us he'd given you twenty-four hours to free the eight political prisoners the government is holding, and then, if they weren't freed, the hostages would begin to pay. My boss played me the tape over the phone. He thought it might be some crazy hoax by the people who'd raided the hotel. He checked with other papers, radio stations, TV. They'd all gotten the same message. Several of them had been sensible enough to tape the call, at least partway through. Same voice."

"Spanish?"

"No, oddly enough. Rather cultivated English voice. I don't mean British, but cultivated, well-educated."

"No name, of course."

"Of course." Wilson's smile faded. "It still sounded pretty wild-eyed to me. I tried to find one or more of the alleged hostages—the girl singer, Sheldon Tranter, our State Department man, Sir George Brooks, who'd been involved in that crazy shooting up on the roof earlier, Ortiz, the OAS man. There wasn't hide nor hair of any of them. That, I guess, made me a believer. I tried Washington and London. No luck. Like you, they claim not to have any plan. That, of course, is hooey! You're all toying with a dozen plans. You really believe them when they tell you they'll give you time?"

"I have to believe," Chambrun said.

"I believe," Sam Yardley said, "and not just because the heat's on. I have some facts you may not have. The eight prisoners these terrorists want released—they aren't all being held in one place. Several of them are in Central America, the rest in different jails in this country."

"So?"

"My people got instructions on the telephone, too."

"The CIA?"

Yardley nodded. "The eight prisoners are all to be flown to an airport in Georgia. A plane must be waiting to fly them overseas—Middle East somewhere. The pilot will get his instructions when the men are on the plane."

"Which gets us where?" Jerry Dodd asked.

"It gets us the time they promised you. It will take at least twenty-four hours to assemble those eight men in one spot and have them airborne."

"Why not just turn them all loose wherever they are?" I asked.

"Because they don't trust us, like we don't trust them," Yardley said. "We are to deliver all eight of them, safe and sound, to some place where they'll be welcomed by friends who are our enemies. The four hostages upstairs will guarantee, they hope, that we'll give in to their demands. They know that it will take at least a day for us to comply."

"And three hours of that day are gone," Chambrun said. "Are they doing anything to move those eight prisoners to an airport in Georgia?"

"I assume they are," Yardley said. "That's just the first step. Since they have means of communicating, they'll know if we are, and they haven't warned you, Mr. Chambrun, to get things moving."

"So you are giving in," Jack Wilson said.

Yardley gave him a tight little smile. "I think we are taking the first steps. We are making it look as though we're giving in. But when they get those eight men to the airport in Georgia, there has to be a final decision. Do we provide them with a plane? Do we fly them to freedom?" He glanced at Chambrun. "You have time to figure out how to save your hotel, Mr. Chambrun. Our people have time to decide whether those four people upstairs are too big a price to pay for turning eight terrorists with a huge following loose to attack us somewhere else."

"You're saying those four people upstairs may not be worth paying their price?" Wilson asked. He sounded as if he couldn't believe it.

"Could be," Yardley said.

"Who makes the decision?" I asked.

Yardley shrugged. "The President, the Prime Minister, the Joint Chiefs, the security experts—everyone who is supposed to be able to make such an evaluation. They're at it now. They may have decided by now."

"Can you find out?" Chambrun asked.

"I doubt it," Yardley said. "Too big a decision to trust to one of their foot soldiers."

Chambrun stood up behind his desk. "So if they won't trust us with answers, we have to make our own decisions."

"Such as?" Jack Wilson asked.

"I'm not going to let those four hostages upstairs be killed in my hotel," Chambrun said.

"How?" Wilson asked.

"When I have the answer to that, Mr. Wilson, I just may let you know," Chambrun said.

PART

TWO

1

"Curiosity killed the cat," my mother used to tell me when I was a kid. The Beaumont was crowded with curious cats when I went down to the lobby. In spite of the fact that hundreds of people were crowding around the front desk in the lobby, trying to check out, they weren't hysterical. They all knew as much as we did from the papers, the radio, and the TV. There was time before a deadline for the bombing. There were what seemed like hundreds of people from the media, demanding to know what the next move was going to be. And there were hundreds of others crowding the bars, the main restaurants, the lobby, hungry to be where the action was that the whole damn world was talking about. I was to discover that no one recognized as being part of the establishment could walk ten feet in the public areas without being swarmed over by people with a thousand questions.

I had gone down from Chambrun's office to the lobby. He wanted a report on how things were going there. Mean Joe Greene couldn't have worked his way across what is usually an open space. Some reporters hemmed me in, and I was suddenly aware that someone was hanging onto my arm as if I was a life raft in a stormy sea. I looked down into the anxious face of a young woman—young meaning in her early twenties.

Superlatives don't always tell a true story, but this girl was something. She had the body of Raquel Welch and the face of an intense angel.

"You're Mark Haskell, aren't you?" she asked. She almost had to shout it over the roar of voices.

"Yes. But look, lady—" I began.

"My father pointed you out to me the other night," she said.

"You should have chosen that moment—" I said, waving at the sea of yammering faces around us.

"I want you to take me to Mr. Chambrun," she said. "My father is Sheldon Tranter. I might be useful."

The daughter of one of the hostages! At that moment Mike Maggio, the night bell captain, who should have been off duty but wasn't, reached me.

"You trying to get somewhere, Mark?" he asked. "I'll run interference for you." He gave the girl an appreciative eye.

"I want to get this lady up to the boss's office," I said.

"Follow me," Mike said.

The Chicago Bears could have used him for a blocking back. It was ten yards to the stairway and Mike lowered his shoulder and made a path for us. I put my arm around the girl and seconds later we were inside the stairway, blocked off by security people. A little breathless, the girl and I both leaned against the wall for a minute.

"If you're some kind of a reporter pulling a fast one on me—" I said.

Her eyelids fluttered. "I am Lois Tranter," she said. "My father is a prisoner up on the twenty-second floor."

"You ready to climb one flight of stairs?" I asked.

"I can climb to the roof if it will help," she said.

Instinct told me it was right to get this girl to Chambrun. As far as I knew, no one connected closely to any of the hostages had been in touch, with the exception of Max London, Hilary Foster's agent, and he hadn't known what was happening when he called to ask for his client. I suppose it was logical for people who didn't know the tight little world that was the Beaumont to make their inquiries to the police, the State Department, Number Ten Downing Street, or even the United Nations. To me the only place of vital importance was Chambrun's second floor office.

"Everything around here is spinning like a top," I told Lois Tranter as we walked along the second-floor corridor toward what I thought of as the hub of the wheel. "You may not get as much time or attention as you hope for."

Her wide blue eyes gave me a steady look. "I am my father's private secretary," she said. "When I said I might be able to help I meant it, Mr. Haskell."

"Try 'Mark,'" I said.

Would you believe we walked right by the door of my apartment, and I never gave a thought to the lovely girl who was waiting there for me to reappear?

A woman from the stenographic pool had taken over the outer office which was Betsy Ruysdale's. I told Lois Tranter to wait there and I went on into the inner sanctum. The people I'd left there were all gone except Sam Yardley, the CIA man, and Betsy. Tony Guardino, the police commissioner's boy, was back. Chambrun gave me a bleak look.

"The police are threatening to order us to get everyone out of the hotel," he said. "Of course I won't leave, nor will I remove my security people, nor anyone else on the staff who volunteers to stay."

Guardino sounded like a man who'd been arguing with a

rock. "So the captain and the crew won't leave the sinking ship," he said. "Maybe you can talk some sense to him, Haskell."

I looked at the boss. "Well, to start with, I volunteer to stay," I said.

"We'll bring in the bomb squad experts," Guardino said. "We need to search every inch of the hotel without interference from curious bystanders."

"You will search every inch of the hotel except the twenty-second floor, where the hostages are being held and where the bomb is located," Chambrun said. "You barge in there and the hostages will start going out the windows. If you try it, you'll have to get past me and my security people."

"You fool," Guardino said, "you've probably got a thousand lives hanging on the whim of those bastards up there."

"I've got a world here that can be fouled up forever if I turn it over to you and your people, Guardino," The Man said.

"Try to listen, just once," Guardino said. "You admit there must be someone on the outside letting them know every move we make. You admit that the raid last night and what's been going on since has been long planned. That a bomb—or bombs—don't have to be up in Twenty-two B. They can be planted anywhere in the hotel, and set off by someone we haven't spotted who's walking around the hotel. Get everyone out of the hotel and you get rid of the potential bomber."

"You argue against yourself, Guardino," Chambrun said. "If it was all long planned—and I think you're right about that—then they've planned for every contingency. Get rid of everyone in the hotel and they have another way to set off the bomb, from somewhere else. I've cleared the twenty-second floor, I'm letting everybody check out who feels nervous about staying. We still have—according to the man on the phone—about twenty hours in which to come up with a sensible plan. Yardley has given us a reason to believe we do have that much time. Tell the commissioner we need time to find an angle before he starts to play hotshot and makes those characters upstairs nervous."

I thought it was time for me to get into the act, maybe give Guardino time to mull over what Chambrun was telling him. I told them I'd taken the liberty of bringing Lois Tranter up from the lobby. "She thinks she might be helpful," I said.

"How?" Chambrun asked.

"She says she's her father's private secretary. No way I could talk to her downstairs."

He turned to Betsy. "Bring her in, Ruysdale."

"I just want to say to you—" Guardino began as Betsy left the room.

"Let's hear what this young woman has to say," Chambrun interrupted him. "We can't afford to pass up anything."

Men are men. When Betsy came in with Lois Tranter I could see both Yardley and Guardino reacting with a little check at a necktie. They hadn't expected a movie star. Chambrun stood up, an unusual courtesy for him in this place where he was king.

"Thank you for coming, Miss Tranter," he said. "Please sit down."

She sat, and I thought a little of her studied composure began to crack. Betsy went to the sideboard and brought her a cup of coffee.

"Is there any news we haven't heard—on the outside?" Lois asked.

"About your father?" Chambrun asked.

Lois nodded.

"Only that he is one of the hostages being held," Chambrun said.

"You have no way of knowing if they're all right, being decently treated?"

"No way."

"You can't ask them? You have a right to be reassured, don't you, if you're meeting their demands?"

Chambrun sat down at his desk again. I don't think I've ever seen him as tired as he looked just then. Going over and over the situation with different people had worn him pretty thin.

"What I have contributed to meeting their demands, Miss Tranter, is really quite secondary," he said. "I've cleared all the other guests and the staff off that floor. I'd have done that whether they'd asked or not. The main decisions about meeting their demands are to be made by people much more important than I am."

"I—I think I understand," she said. "But you are in touch with them!"

"They are not taking any in-calls," Chambrun said. "The out-calls they've made so far have been made public—by them, not the hotel."

"But you've asked about my father, and the others?"

"I've been told what will happen to the hostages if we try to cross the people who are holding them," Chambrun said.

"Oh, my God!" she said. She lifted her hands to her lovely face for a moment, trying to hide what she obviously felt.

"I don't want to pressure you, Lois," Chambrun said, "but you must understand that the heat is on. Mr. Yardley, here, is from the CIA. Mr. Guardino is from the New York

70

police. We have only a few hours in which to make what could be final and fatal decisions. You told Mark Haskell that you might be able to help us."

She was silent for a moment and then lowered her hands. Her courage had returned. You could almost see it flowing back into her.

"My father and I were having drinks in the Trapeze Bar, night before last," she said. "About six o'clock in the evening."

"You're not registered here in the hotel with your father," Chambrun said.

"No. Our home is in Washington. I'm staying with friends here in the city, but Dad invited me to join him for drinks and dinner."

"Why was he staying here and not with friends?" Chambrun asked.

"Professional reasons—politics," she said. "There were people staying here who were important to him and he wanted to be close to them."

"Who were those people?" Chambrun asked.

"Dad is an expert on Central America," Lois said. "There are people here from the Organization of American States—Mr. Ortiz, who is one of the hostages and who was staying in Suite Twenty-two B. There was Sir George Brooks, who is another of the hostages. He was involved in the Falkland Islands war and knows that part of the world inside out. Others whose names I don't know."

"How does that help us, Lois?"

"I was just answering your questions," Lois said. "But the other night in the Trapeze . . ." She hesitated and drew a deep breath. "I'd never been there before. My father told me it was the place to go to see some of the most interesting people in the world. He pointed some of them out to me." She glanced at me. "You were one of them, Mark, and there were a couple of movie stars, and a famous Texas oil tycoon, and others who didn't mean anything to me then or now. But then Dad turned serious. 'That man at the bar,' he said, pointing out a nice-looking middle-aged man who was drinking by himself. 'He may be one of the most dangerous men in the world—or at least, my world,' Dad said. I asked him what the man's name was. 'He's used a dozen different names in his time,' Dad said. 'God knows what he's calling himself now.' I asked him in what way this man was dangerous. 'I wouldn't want to meet him alone in a dark alley,' Dad said. 'Looks like a nice, friendly creature, doesn't he? He's a terrorist, a revolutionary, a plotter against everything democracy stands for. He helps provide arms and mercenaries and sophisticated technology for the people who are our enemies in Central America.' 'And he stands around here, in public? Why isn't he arrested?' I asked. Dad laughed. 'Most of the most important criminals in the world walk around scot-free,' he told me. 'We never get them for their crimes. Maybe income-tax evasion or something absurd like that.' I was surprised to see a shudder shake my father. 'I should have known he would be here where his particular world is under discussion.' 'Is he dangerous to you?' I asked. 'He's dangerous to anyone who gets in his way,' Dad said."

"He never told you the man's name?"

"No."

"Would you know this man if you saw him again?"

"I remember looking back at the bar after Dad told me all this, but the man was gone. I think I'd recognize him. I've been looking for him ever since last night's raid and Dad's disappearance. But the hotel has been so jammed with people . . ." She shrugged. "If I saw him again I'm sure I'd know him."

"That's it?" Chambrun asked, when she didn't go on.

"One other thing that may not be related at all," Lois said. "There was a fabulous-looking old, old lady sitting at a corner table, surrounded by people who seemed to be enjoying her conversation. She had a little black-and-white dog sitting on a red cushion on a chair specially provided for it."

Chambrun glanced at me. Victoria Haven! She went to the Trapeze every late afternoon with Toto and held court there. Our old lady with what she called "my Japanese gentleman friend." Toto!

"My Dad pointed out this lady to me. 'Extraordinary woman,' he said. 'She could tell you a lot about terrorism. Many years ago she was kidnapped in Central America, held as a hostage until a revolutionary prisoner was released. Nobody was ever arrested for that crime, either.' 'Your man at the bar?' I asked him. 'Lord, no,' Dad said. 'He'd hardly been born when that happened.'" Lois gave Chambrun an unhappy look. "This isn't much, after all, is it?"

"If you saw the man at the bar again it might be," Chambrun said.

"I'll keep looking," Lois said. "But if he is involved with what's happened to Dad, he won't appear again, will he?"

"He has no way of knowing what your father told you while you were watching him," Chambrun said.

"With the hotel apparently bulging with people on the Central American scene," Yardley said, "Sheldon Tranter surely wasn't the only person around who knew this man at the bar and what he stood for. There must be others who saw him hanging around the Trapeze. When the raid came and the hostages were taken, he'd make himself scarce, wouldn't he?"

"Maybe Miss Tranter can give a police artist a good enough description of this man so that he could make a picture that could be circulated among the Central American people here," Guardino said. "We might be able to put a name to him. Would you do that, Miss Tranter?"

"I don't quite understand," she said.

"Some of our police artists are amazing," Guardino said. "You start with a tall, dark man—he draws a sketch—you tell him broader shoulders—he fixes that—you tell him thicker eyebrows—he fixes that—you say wider mouth—and he fixes that. Eventually you say yes, he looked pretty much like that."

"Of course I would do that," Lois said.

"Use your phone?" Guardino asked Chambrun. "I'll get one of our guys up here."

While Guardino called police headquarters for an artist, Chambrun, with Yardley joining in, went back to Lois Tranter.

"If you are your father's private secretary," Chambrun said, "you must know exactly what his mission is here in New York."

"What seems like an endless debate," Lois said. I had the feeling she was well informed. "Should we have battleships, and planes, and so-called 'advisers' in the area, or should we let the people there settle their own problems? The OAS people think if we would withdraw, the chances for peace would be greater."

"And your father?"

"Dad has to represent the State Department's view, no matter what his own feelings may be," Lois said.

74

"And the State Department's view is?"

"The President says that naval and military exercises in that area have been going on for a long time, long before his administration and the ones before it. Some native people have called it 'gunboat diplomacy' for years. We decide one side is legitimate and we support it with money and weapons and technical help. When the side we're supporting is thrown out of power by revolution, we tend to support the new power, though they have been our enemies before that. There are investments and property that are important to us. That kind of flip-flopping has been going on for generations, according to Dad."

"So he's for playing it the way we've always played it?" Yardley asked.

"He thinks things are different now," Lois said. "It's not just internal revolutions now. The Russians are in the picture, supporting the anti-government forces with money and arms and technology. It's really a conflict between the two major world powers, with the Central American people just pawns in the game. He thinks all the political talk about conservatives and radicals among the Central American people is garbage. Will we let communist Russia take over Central America, as they have Cuba, and have our major enemy on our doorstep? All the pious talk about democracy versus communism is hogwash, Dad thinks. It's power against power. We may be supporting evil governments who ignore human rights and democratic philosophies, but they are prepared to fight our major enemy and we have to stand by them."

"That's commonly accepted as the State Department view and your father articulates it," Chambrun said. "Somebody has called it 'the big stick approach.' But privately, how does your father feel?"

Lois gave the boss a tight little smile. "We could spend all day on that, Mr. Chambrun. I guess you could say Dad thinks we talk a great game—morality, human rights, fair play, the whole bag of high principles, and covertly—Dad says our whole society is based on the word 'covert,' secret, undercover—covertly we support profits for the already very rich, and to hell with the morality of how they get it." She leaned forward in her chair. "Enough of that. What are you going to do, Mr. Chambrun?"

"Do?"

"About my father and the other hostages!"

Chambrun glanced at his watch. "We still have time to come to a decision about that."

I knew, and so did Lois, that he was saying he hadn't an idea about what he could do.

"If something happens to my father," Lois said, and her soft voice had taken on a rough edge, "I want you to know that I'll remember that you sat here doing absolutely nothing!"

He gave her a steady look. "What would you do, Miss Tranter? Would you charge the citadel and let them drop your father out the window while we batter down the door?"

The color faded from her face. "I'd make a deal, no matter what it cost," she said.

"They've offered us a deal. Four hostages for eight prisoners flown to a safe place."

"So make it," she said.

"That decision will be made by the president and Mrs. Thatcher and God knows who else," Chambrun said.

"And suppose they agree," Yardley said, in his quiet voice. "Will they set your father free then to tell us who they are and put them under the gun?"

"If you really want to help, Lois," Chambrun said, "perhaps you can come up with a suggestion that this exhausted mind hasn't covered."

Lois lifted her hands to her face again, and this time I knew she was fighting tears.

Chambrun had been showing the hanging-judge side of his personality since last night's raid, but the other side of the coin, I knew, was a man of real compassion. He got up from his desk and walked around to where Lois was sitting covering her face. He put a hand gently on her shoulder.

"Don't give up on us entirely, Lois," he said. "I wouldn't have lived as long as I have if I hadn't been able to come up with answers in a crisis." He turned to face the rest of us. "I'm worried about Victoria Haven," he said. "I think I'll go up to her penthouse to see her. You people can hold the fort for half an hour, can't you?"

"I'm sure she's all right," I said. "If you'd like me to check on her—"

"It's probably absurd," Chambrun said, "but somehow I can't separate her from what's going on here. 'Remember to kill me' forty-five years ago—and then it comes up last night. Sheldon Tranter saw her the night before last and remembered about her. Maybe she can dredge up something she hasn't thought was important."

"What if the guy in Twenty-two B calls you?" I asked.

"Have them switch the call to Victoria's penthouse," he said. At the door he turned back to us. "I have a head full of rocks at the moment. Maybe moving around the hotel a little will help get rid of them."

Somehow I felt lost when the door closed behind him. He was the one chance we had for a sensible answer, and he admitted he was lost. Yardley had one set of facts and ideas and a special force behind him; Guardino had another set of facts and another kind of force. They didn't have answers, though. Betsy Ruysdale knew The Man better than any of us, but if he had rocks in his head she must have rocks in hers.

Johnny Thacker had been ordered to have the department chiefs here in half an hour. That was some time ago. Had Chambrun forgotten? I found myself obsessed by the little electric clock on The Man's desk, the second hand moving steadily round and round. Time wasn't going to hold back for any of us.

Guardino broke the heavy silence in the room. "A police artist is on his way, Miss Tranter," he said. "Do you mind waiting here for him?"

Lois shook her head. She was still fighting tears.

"I need a private phone where I can talk to Washington," Yardley said.

Betsy beckoned to him. There was an extension in Chambrun's dressing room and she took Yardley there.

"The commissioner isn't going to like our just waiting around, twiddling our thumbs and doing nothing," Guardino said. "He's going to demand action."

"Let him suggest something that will work," I said. "It must be nice to sit downtown, blocks from here, in a big air-conditioned office, away from the noise and the turmoil and the smell of the fear of death, and demand action!"

"I'm here to see for him, listen for him—smell for him, if you like," Guardino said. "I haven't advised him to do anything—yet. I feel a little like Chambrun—rocks in my head. You freeze when you realize that anything you do may cost you more than you want to pay."

"Thanks for sounding like a human being," I said.

Guardino gave me a wry smile. "It's not easy," he said. "You think Chambrun will come up with something?"

"He always has," I said.

Doing nothing was the worst thing of all. I decided to go find Johnny Thacker and tell them not to sweat trying to get the people Chambrun wanted to see. The Boss had taken off and wouldn't be back for at least another half hour.

The lobby was, if anything, more of a madhouse than it had been earlier. The terrorists up in Twenty-two B had made the situation so public that we were drawing the curious like flies. I spotted Johnny Thacker on the fringes of the mob that was crowding around the checkout desk.

"Most of the upper floors are emptying out," he told me. "I couldn't get the people the boss wanted right now. Would you believe that, with all the cops and security people, we've got pickpockets, and three or four gals have had gold chains snatched off their necks? We need everyone we've got to keep kooks from filtering upstairs. Atterbury and the other people on checkout are going bananas."

"I'll let you know when the boss gets back," I said.

As I turned away from Johnny I saw Jerry Dodd trying to wigwag me from over by the elevators. I elbowed my way through reporters and rubberneckers to where our security chief stood. As I approached him I realized that the tall, blond man standing next to him, was with him, not just part of the mob. Jerry must have explained to this guy who I was because he didn't identify me.

"Mark, this is Inspector Stanley Brooks, from Scotland Yard in London," Jerry said.

"Brooks?" I asked. I couldn't hear myself and realized you had to shout to be heard over the roar of hundreds of excited voices.

Inspector Brooks gave me the cold look of a state trooper asking to see your driver's license. "My brother is one of the hostages being held upstairs," he said. "I'm here to get him free."

"Lucky you're here in New York," I said.

"Wasn't when I got the news," Brooks said. "These bloody bastards who have George called Lord Huntingdon in London at five in the morning, our time. Huntingdon got in touch with me and I asked to be assigned."

"But you're here! It isn't noon yet!"

"Modern miracles," Jerry said.

Inspector Brooks, quite matter-of-fact, explained that the Concorde jet leaves London at 10:30 A.M., their time, and arrives here at 9:25 our time.

"Gets here an hour before it started," Jerry said. "The inspector wants to see the boss, but someone's been on the phone up there for the last fifteen minutes."

"Yardley calling Washington," I said. I told Brooks that Yardley was a CIA man. "Assistant to the police commissioner is up there, too. Mr. Chambrun isn't, but he'll be back shortly. You might as well come up there and wait, Inspector, out of this jungle."

"Where is the boss?" Jerry asked.

"Went up to the roof to talk to Mrs. Haven," I said.

We went past the security men guarding the stairway and walked up to the second floor.

"Mrs. Haven is the woman someone shot at?" Brooks asked as we were climbing. He was up on everything—but wasn't the whole damned world? "Lucky escape."

"Your brother may have saved her life," I said. "He responded so quickly to the outcry set up by Mrs. Haven's little dog that the gunman didn't have a second chance at the lady."

"Too bad he couldn't have been as efficient at protecting

himself," Brooks said. "Do we know when or where he was captured?"

"Just a guess," Jerry Dodd answered. "After our people responded to his phone call and the doctor told us that Mrs. Haven wasn't seriously hurt, your brother must have gone down to the lobby to see what was going on there. Natural curiosity."

"Damn foolishness," Inspector Brooks said. "Nobody saw him?"

"You've seen what it's like down there, Inspector. You couldn't spot your own mother unless you tripped over her. Nobody was looking for him, nobody saw him. After we knew he was one of the hostages, I spoke to some of our responsible people who would have known him by sight. No luck. They'd been fighting off an army of goons, not looking for a familiar face. People were coming and going like a tidal wave, Inspector."

"George should have been able to take care of himself," the British cop said. "He's a tough customer." He gave Jerry a grim look. "Well, so am I!"

Chambrun wasn't going to be happy with him, I thought; an angry brother trying to strong-arm his way to a rescue.

Yardley and Betsy Ruysdale were still missing when we reached Chambrun's office. Inspector Brooks looked around as though he thought he must be in the wrong place. The office, with its magnificent Oriental rug, the carved Florentine desk, the Picasso painting on the wall, looked more like an elegant living room than a place of business.

Guardino and Lois Tranter were there with a young man I hadn't seen before. He was obviously the police artist. He was working on a large sketch pad on Chambrun's desk, with Guardino and the girl looking over his shoulder.

Guardino broke away and introduced himself, expressed

his surprise that the inspector could have gotten here so quickly, and explained what was going on.

"Bill Pollard is a genius at this sort of thing," he said, nodding toward the artist and Lois. "I'd like not to interrupt the process if you don't mind, Inspector."

"I'm a great deal more interested in what you're planning to do about the situation upstairs," Brooks said.

"The final decision will come from the heads of your government and ours," Guardino said.

Inspector Brooks gave him a cold look. "They will decide whether or not to free the prisoners," he said. "After that, if they free them, we can keep our fingers crossed and hope they'll let the hostages go, which I find unlikely. If they don't free the revolutionaries, then what happens to my brother, and that girl's father, will be a matter of luck, probably bad luck."

Guardino grinned. "You're right, of course," he said.

"You may care who wins a war in Central America, Guardino, but let me tell you that I don't give a damn about anything but the safety of my brother!" He brought a clenched fist down in the palm of his other hand. "With or without your help, Guardino, or the hotel's help, or God's help, I'm going to get George out of there!" He took a deep breath. "If you people have a plan, I'll listen to it. If I can't go for it, I'll handle things my own way."

Guardino was about to have back at him, I thought, when Pollard, the police artist, followed by Lois Tranter, came over to us from the desk.

"This seems to be as close as we can come," Pollard said, holding out his sketch pad.

He had drawn a picture of a tall, dark man standing at a bar with a drink in his hand. It was a pleasant face with heavy black eyebrows and a wide, rather determined-looking mouth with a small black mustache on the upper lip. It was familiar, but I couldn't recall where I'd seen him. Then suddenly I realized I was being reminded of the late actor Clark Gable.

"Clark Gable," Jerry Dodd said, echoing my reaction.

"I remember thinking that when my father pointed him out to me," Lois Tranter said.

"That made it easy," Pollard said.

"I don't know why you're drawing pictures of this chap," Inspector Brooks said, "but I know him, and there is one detail wrong with the picture."

"You know him?" Jerry said.

Brooks nodded. "The King of Terror, he's called. He's had a hundred names since he's been on our wanted files in London. I think his real name is Ricardo Avilla, though that may also be an alias."

I felt my muscles go tense. Avilla was the name of the man who had kidnapped Victoria Haven forty-five years ago. Not possibly this man, but the same last name!

"What's wrong with the drawing?" Pollard, the artist, asked.

"You have him holding that drink in his right hand," Brooks said.

"He's left-handed?" Pollard asked, reaching for his drawing pencil.

"He doesn't *have* a right hand," Brooks said. "Lost it in some kind of a violence early on in his life. He wears a plastic hand, usually covered by a black glove—and usually hidden in his jacket pocket."

Pollard began fiddling with his drawing, erasing, redrawing.

"It shouldn't be hard to spot a man with an artificial hand," Jerry Dodd said.

I explained to Brooks why we were interested; that Sheldon Tranter had pointed this character out to his daughter the night before the raid, drinking in the Trapeze.

"I didn't notice about the hand," Lois said. "My father didn't mention it and I had no reason to notice which hand he used to hold his drink."

"I think we better get Chambrun back down here," I said. "The man who kidnapped Mrs. Haven forty-five years ago was named Avilla, Carlos Avilla. This drawing might revive something in Mrs. Haven's memory."

"I can give you a history on this one," Brooks said, jabbing a forefinger at the drawing. "He couldn't have been more than five or six years old forty-five years ago. He is, however, quite capable of having masterminded this whole damned adventure here."

Yardley was still on the extension of Chambrun's phone, and so I went to the outer office and asked the switchboard to call Mrs. Haven's penthouse. The lady answered almost immediately after the first ring.

"Mark Haskell here, Mrs. Haven," I said. "I'd like to speak to Mr. Chambrun."

"So would I," the lady said.

"He isn't there with you?"

"What made you think he would be?" she asked.

"He started up to see you almost half an hour ago," I said.

"Well, he never made it, Mark. Is there something wrong?"

"This whole place is topsy-turvy," I said. "He got waylaid somewhere. If he gets to you before I find him will you tell him he's urgently needed down here?"

"Of course. He isn't in danger, is he, Mark?"

I hadn't thought so, but I was suddenly aware of the small hairs rising on the back of my neck.

"If anyone can take care of himself it's the boss," I said, and hoped I was right.

Back in Chambrun's office I told Jerry and the others that the boss hadn't arrived at Mrs. Haven's place yet.

"There are five thousand reporters in this bughouse," Jerry said. "They probably cornered him before he could get started."

"I'm going to find him," I said. I didn't want to mention the anxiety I was feeling in front of the others. They didn't seem to think there was anything unusual about the circumstances. When Chambrun sets out to do something he does it, five thousand reporters or not.

"I'll go with you," Jerry said.

"Tell Miss Ruysdale when she comes back, will you?" I asked Guardino.

"Somebody better bloody well come up with a plan of action," Inspector Brooks said. "I'm not waiting very much longer."

Jerry was suddenly angry. "Before you decide on some harebrained scheme of your own, Inspector, you better be damn sure it makes some sense!"

Jerry and I walked down the hall and down the stairway to the lobby.

"I know how that limey must feel," Jerry said. "His brother! But he could blow something before we're ready."

There were two of Jerry's men guarding the entrance to the stairway at the lobby level.

"Mr. Chambrun come down this way a while back?" Jerry asked.

"Yeah. Headed for the roof, he told us," one of the men said.

"He was headed for the elevators," the other one said.

We edged our way out into the crush of people. There are six elevators in the west bank. The doors to all of them were closed, lights off in the cars. The regular operators in their blue uniforms were standing guard in front of those closed doors. Only the two cars at the far end of the row went up to the roof. Jerry and I reached the two operators on those cars.

"Either of you see Mr. Chambrun?" Jerry asked.

The one named Pat Mullins gestured toward the ceiling. "He went up to his place," he said.

"You took him up, Pat?" Jerry said.

"No," Pat said. "He took himself. He said I must be pooped out like everyone else. Told me to go get myself a cup of coffee and take a few minutes off. He didn't want anyone going up to the roof, anyway, and he could handle the car."

"I see it's there, so he must have come down," Jerry said.

Mullins shook his head. "Sent it down on the automatic," he said. "It was here when I came back from my coffee."

It wasn't too unusual for Chambrun to operate a car, particularly late at night. Only one of the two roof cars would have an operator on it after one in the morning. Chambrun would often use the car that was out of use for his private transportation. If he was going up to stay he would often send the car back to the lobby on the automatic gadget. When you get to the top you open the door, press the button for the lobby on the automatic, step out, close the door, and the car goes down.

Jerry turned to me. "You have a key to the boss's penthouse, don't you, Mark?"

Betsy Ruysdale and I were specially privileged. If Chambrun wants something in his penthouse I can fetch for him. Betsy, I think, has other reasons for having a key.

"We can handle the car, Pat," Jerry said.

Pat opened the locked door for us and we headed for the roof.

"It's not like him," Jerry said, "but I've never seen him so tired before. He could have gone to his place, decided to lie down for a couple of minutes, and conked out."

I didn't believe that for a minute, but it was something to go on. There were still two of Jerry's men stationed on the roof and one in Mrs. Haven's penthouse. Neither of the men on the roof had seen Chambrun.

"If the elevator had come up we'd have been waiting," one of the men said. "We'd have been right there when he got off the car."

I used my key to get into Chambrun's place. He wasn't there, nor was there any sign that he'd been there recently. The maids had done their cleanup job that morning and everything was neat as a pin, no butts in the ashtrays, no coffee cup where it shouldn't be.

We walked across the roof to Mrs. Haven's place. She'd seen us arrive and was waiting for us.

"Still looking for Pierre?" she asked.

"I guess he hasn't made it up here," I said. I brought her as nearly up to date as I could; the arrival of Sir George Brooks's brother and Lois Tranter's appearance on the scene.

"Nobody has decided yet just what they will do?" Mrs. Haven asked.

"Different people with different interests," I said. "They haven't gotten together yet on any plan."

"Time keeps passing," Mrs. Haven said. "What is it Pierre wants of me?"

"As far as we know, the person who shot at you is still walking around free. I guess he wondered if there was anything you'd forgotten to tell us in the excitement of the moment."

"I never saw anything or anyone," Mrs. Haven said. "I heard the first shot, just as I was struck, and had the presence of mind to duck."

"You told me about your kidnapping forty-five years ago," I said. "Man named Carlos Avilla."

I told her about Lois Tranter's father pointing out a character at the Trapeze Bar, the police artist's improvisation, and Inspector Brooks's identifying him as one Ricardo Avilla.

The old lady gave me an incredulous look. "There was a child," she said, "Carlos Avilla's grandson. His name was Ricardo. Six, seven, eight years old at the time. A charming little boy who stayed with his grandfather at the camp where I was held. The child spent a lot of time with me, begging me to teach him English."

"Kid look like Clark Gable?" Jerry Dodd asked.

"I can't imagine Clark Gable at seven years old," Mrs. Haven said. Her eyes clouded. "Carlos Avilla, the grandfather and my captor, *did* look a little like Gable! Dark, handsome, big ears! Do you suppose—?"

"The man Tranter pointed out to his daughter had lost his right hand in some kind of an accident," Jerry said.

Mrs. Haven's eyes widened. "The child, Ricardo, has lost his right hand!" she said. "Some kind of guerrilla raid and bombing in one of their endless wars down there."

"That's our man," Jerry said, "grown up!"

"If he looks enough like his grandfather for you to recognize him, plus the right hand missing, that may account for the attempt to put you out of business, Mrs. Haven," I said.

"I'd like to see that police artist's drawing," Mrs. Haven said. "I'll go down with you. Pierre will surely turn up in his office, and then he can ask me what he wants to ask me."

"It's safer for you to stay here, well guarded," Jerry said.

"I can't bear staying up here, not knowing what's going on," the lady said. "If I'm not safe in Pierre's office, I'm not safe anywhere!"

I hoped she was right, but that wasn't what concerned me at the moment. Where had Chambrun got to? He had disappeared somewhere between the lobby and the roof.

People in high places may have been concerned about a confrontation between the two great world powers, a nuclear war, and control of the world; Lois Tranter and Inspector Brooks were concerned about the hostages in Twenty-two B; but in a very short time several hundred members of the work force at the Beaumont were concerned with only one thing. Where was The Man?

There had certainly never been a time in my ten years on Chambrun's staff when he couldn't have been reached within minutes of his being needed. He never let his whereabouts be a mystery. If he left his office, the girls on the switchboard and Betsy Ruysdale knew where he could be reached. He had told us this time where he was going. If the man in Twenty-two B called he was to be switched to Mrs. Haven's penthouse. If he'd changed his plans voluntarily he would have let us know—under normal conditions. There were security men or police on every floor of the hotel except Twenty-two West. If he had left the elevator he was running on any floor but Twenty-two he would have been spotted. It took what seemed an endless time to check with everyone guarding thirty-nine floors, but in the end we came up empty. No one had seen the boss. The last person known to have a contact with him was Pat Mullins, the elevator operator he'd sent off to have a coffee while he took over Mullins's elevator himself.

"The last I saw him he was standing in the open door of the car, watching me take off," Mullins told us.

"You saw him get in the car, close the door, and start up?" Jerry Dodd asked Mullins.

"No, I mean, I was glad to take the break he offered me. I wasn't concerned about him. He's run that car himself a thousand times."

"So you didn't see him actually start up?"

"No. There wasn't any reason to wait and watch him go," Mullins said. "Is there some reason I should have?"

"I'm not blaming you for anything, Pat. I'm just trying to find a clue."

"He changed his mind after Pat left," Betsy Ruysdale suggested, her face ghost-white. "He didn't go up, or he changed his mind partway up and came back down while Pat was still missing."

"Or he decided to be a big shot and face it out with the characters in Twenty-two B," Guardino suggested.

"In which case they now have five hostages," Inspector Brooks said.

That was something I just couldn't buy. The last thing in the world Chambrun would try was some kind of James Bond heroics. He was a man who, in all my experience with him, added up the pluses and the minuses and played it the way the odds suggested. He might be reckless about himself but never about his hotel or the people in it.

While we had been trying to check every possible base,

Victoria Haven, accompanied by her security guards, had arrived in Chambrun's office. There was the elegance of a queen about this great lady. She had gone directly to Chambrun's desk where Pollard, the artist, and Lois Tranter were still fiddling with the dream-up of the man at the bar. She took a quick look at the drawing and turned away. Something about her commanded everyone's attention.

I quickly introduced her to Yardley, Guardino, and Inspector Brooks.

"I may owe my life to your brother's quick action, Inspector," she said. "How can I help?"

"Persuade some of these people to concentrate on how to get him free instead of looking for a man who is perfectly competent to take care of himself," Brooks said. His anger was barely under control.

"The drawing, Mrs. Haven," Guardino said.

"A long time ago," she began, "forty-five years ago—"

"I think most of us are familiar with at least the outlines of that time in your life, Mrs. Haven," Yardley said.

"That drawing could be of Carlos Avilla, the man who abducted me back then," Mrs. Haven said. "It can't be, of course, if he is someone Miss Tranter saw in the Trapeze night before last. Carlos Avilla would be well over a hundred years old now—if he is alive."

"Miss Tranter tells us you were in the Trapeze at the same time her father pointed out the man at the bar to her, the man in the drawing. You could have seen him."

She gave him a little smile. "At my age, Mr. Guardino, there are little vanities. Standing ten feet away from me, as you are, your face is a blur. I need these to see you clearly." She opened her purse and took out a pair of horn-rimmed glasses. "I don't like to wear these unless I have to." She put them on and they gave her an unexpectedly owlish look. I'd never seen her wear them before. She took them off. "I was surrounded by friends in the Trapeze," she said. "I didn't need to be looking for someone I might know. I had all the company I needed. Without these glasses I couldn't have seen the man Miss Tranter's father pointed out to her."

"The child without a hand you mentioned to Jerry and me upstairs," I said.

"A bright, charming little boy of about seven who had lost his right hand in some sort of bombing outrage," Mrs. Haven said. "His name was Ricardo."

"That's our man," Brooks said.

"Just because of the coincidence that I may have known him forty-five years ago?" Mrs. Haven asked.

"In my world, in Yardley's world, in Guardino's world, Ricardo Avilla is a genius at terror, an architect of violence. Put him down in a place where there is terror and violence, like this hotel, and you simply can't believe it's a coincidence," Inspector Brooks said.

"The man on the outside who has a way to communicate with the people on the inside—in Twenty-two B," Guardino said.

"You think he is the man who came up to the roof after the raid started and tried to kill me?" Mrs. Haven asked, looking around for an answer from any of us.

Inspector Brooks shrugged. "He saw you in the Trapeze Bar," he said. "He didn't know about your vision problem. He supposed you'd seen him and could identify him. After the violence started, you'd remember and report his presence to the police."

92

"If it was that important that I not remember him," Mrs. Haven said, "why didn't he keep trying to finish me off?"

"Your dog," Brooks said, "brought my brother out on the run from his penthouse. George would have recognized Avilla, and Avilla couldn't risk a shoot-out with George. He had to take the chance that you wouldn't remember in the excitement, or with the possible physical pain you might be suffering from your wound. Avilla is apparently important to whatever their plans are in the next few hours. He had to take the chance—if you'll forgive me, Mrs. Haven—that a very old woman just might not remember after all."

"All you have at my time of life, Inspector, are memories." She smiled at him. "If you've still got all your marbles. And let me assure you I have!"

"If Avilla is part of this whole operation, he must have known Tranter by sight," Guardino said.

"But Tranter wasn't going to be able to talk after the fact," Brooks said. "Tranter was to be a hostage."

"Miss Tranter? She was there in the bar with her father."

"Avilla had no way of guessing that Tranter was giving his daughter a rundown on him," Brooks said. "Chances are, Avilla didn't think Tranter would recognize him. Had they had any direct contact that you know of, Miss Tranter?"

Lois shook her head. "My father didn't say, but there was no question that he knew Avilla by sight. My father has spent most of the last ten years of his life in Central America. Ricardo Avilla is a public figure down there. Thousands of people would know him by sight, including foreign observers like my father."

"One thing is certain," Guardino said. "We must circulate copies of this drawing to all your security people, Dodd, and to all the cops. If Avilla is still prowling the hotel, he could just be the key that would open the door of Twenty-two B to us."

I didn't say so just then, but Avilla might also be the person who could tell us where Chambrun was. I felt a cool hand slip into mine. It was Lois Tranter's.

"Let me help you look, Mark," she said. It was almost a whisper. "I want to find him just as badly as you do."

Bright girl, I thought. She could read minds.

2

We were, I thought much later, like kids who needed the support and approval of an all-wise papa. Guardino and Yardley, a couple of pretty tough cookies, were in luck. They didn't have the authority to determine what was to be done about what was going on in the Beaumont, or at an airport in Georgia, or in half a dozen prisons around the world. They could "suggest," come up with their "best judgments," but they knew that their Great White Fathers were in Washington and in police headquarters in Manhattan. The final decision would be made for them. They would never have to take responsibility for the eventual outcome.

I wasn't so sure about Inspector Brooks. He was a tough, strong, impassioned man, caring deeply for a brother in danger, thousands of miles away from his Great White Father—or was it Mother?—and trying to justify to himself taking an action on his own. He could be dangerous to us, to his brother, and to the other hostages if he made a wrong move. Looking at him I could almost see wrong moves, cooking like a boiling pot, behind his angry eyes. We had to sit on him somehow.

Betsy Ruysdale, Jerry Dodd and I, and a large, well-trained staff of people in the Beaumont were much worse off than those others. We had been trained over our working lives at the hotel to depend on Chambrun for any critical decisions that had to be made. He had always, would always, *must* always make the key moves, and he would always, had always, been willing to take the full blame if something didn't work. We were geared, equipped, and prepared to take any order he gave, any action he demanded of us. Without him to give the orders, plan the action, we were responsible for his hotel, his world, his future. I could see him now, staring at us, the hanging judge, letting us know that we had taken an action that any idiot should have known could only lead to disaster.

"Who is in charge of the hotel in Chambrun's absence?" Guardino asked.

It was a good question. Chambrun rarely left the hotel. The world came to him, he didn't go out to it. Maybe once or twice a year he would go to the theater, and we would know the theater's phone number and his seat number. I used to kid him about the way the city had changed in the thirty-odd years he had been the Beaumont's manager. "You could get lost if you went out there alone," I have told him.

"Nothing that really matters to me is anywhere outside the walls of my hotel," he would tell me. "The day I get lost in my hotel it will be time to send for psychiatric help."

Was this that day? Had he cracked under the pressure of what was going on inside the walls of his hotel? That was nonsense, I told myself.

"We are set up to handle every aspect of the running of the hotel," Betsy Ruysdale told Guardino.

"I don't doubt that for a minute—under normal circumstances," Guardino said. "But did you have contingency plans for a raid on your hotel, like last night's? Are you prepared for hundreds of guests leaving at the same time? The confusion in the lobby indicates that you aren't. Do you have a blueprint for action in case of a bomb or a major fire?"

"I can answer 'yes' to that last," Jerry Dodd said.

"Does that include an invasion by vandals at the critical moment?" Guardino asked.

Jerry gave the police commissioner's man a sour look. "It does not include a way to handle violence after a free concert in the park which the police couldn't handle," he said.

"If what happened here had anything to do with the free concert, you've got me there," Guardino said without anger. "I don't believe for a moment that the characters who raided the hotel had anything to do with the concert or were ever there. The concert was used to divert our attention from the real situation."

"So, I give you that," Jerry said.

"Suppose I suggest to the commissioner that the hotel be evacuated—all the guests, all the staff and help—and that he deploy a trained SWAT team to take over, deal with the characters in Twenty-two B, stage an armed rescue of the hostages if it comes to that?"

Jerry's face was a frozen mask. "I guess you could order all the guests to leave the hotel and be obeyed," he said. "I guess you can bar the curious public and the press from coming in. But I can tell you that not one member of the staff, and in particular my security people, will leave their posts without orders from The Man."

"Chambrun?"

"Who else?" Jerry said.

"What you're saying is that Chambrun, who has disappeared, who may be dead, his body stuffed into a trash can somewhere, is still in charge?"

"Something like that," Jerry said. "Our orders are to keep everyone off the twenty-second floor, and that we'll do, whether they are vandals or cops."

"Pierre is not dead," Mrs. Victoria Haven said in a clear, strong voice.

"How do you know that, Mrs. Haven?" Guardino asked.

"I would know," the old lady said, "because if Pierre was dead my heart would have stopped beating. You and Jerry, and everyone else who cares, have two people to find. First there is Pierre. But really, first there is this Ricardo Avilla, with his artificial hand, who can, undoubtedly, tell you where Pierre is."

"I would like to help find this Avilla," Lois Tranter broke in. "I would know him if I saw him, hand or no hand."

"And he knows that," Sam Yardley said, speaking for the first time. He moved in on us. "I've been sitting here, waiting for that damn phone to ring. If Avilla and his friends in Twenty-two B are responsible for Chambrun's absence, they will use that to bring extra pressure of some kind on us."

"And at least we'd know that Chambrun isn't wandering around somewhere whistling Dixie!" Guardino said. "So, if you are in charge, Mr. Dodd—"

"I'm in charge of hotel security," Jerry said.

"If you *were* in charge, what would your next move be?" Guardino asked. "I'm trying to tell you, friend, that I respect your judgment, will pay attention to your opinion."

"Thanks," Jerry said. He fished a cigarette out of the pack in his pocket and snapped his lighter into flame. "If I had a decision to make I'd have to know about other decisions. I'd have to know what Washington intends to do about the political prisoners—really intends to do. I'd have to know what London intends to do. I'd have to know what the OAS boys are advising. I'd have to know just how

98

important the hostages up in Twenty-two B are to them."

"They're assembling the prisoners at that airport in Georgia," Yardley said.

"But do they intend to set them free when it comes down to the wire?" Jerry asked. "I suggest that you haven't been told, Yardley, and that Guardino and the Police Commissioner haven't been told."

Nobody protested that notion.

"If they're playing it on the level and the prisoners are being flown to Georgia, then I advise sitting tight and waiting till the last minute on the chance that the hostages upstairs will be set free."

"Or used further by their captors to get themselves free," Yardley said.

"If that's their plan they'll tell us," Jerry said.

"And then?"

"Then I would have to think the hostages don't have a chance. They know too much," Jerry said. "If the terrorists discover that Washington and London are double-crossing them, the hostages don't have a chance either. In those two situations, either of them, I would attempt a rescue; a simultaneous attack, back and front, on Twenty-two B. Properly planned and timed, we just might save one or two of the hostages."

"Oh, my God!" Lois Tranter whispered.

"One or two is better than none, Miss Tranter," Jerry said.

"You don't have anyone up there you care about," Inspector Brooks said, in a voice that was a growl.

"I care about them all, Inspector," Jerry said, "which is more than I can say for you." He glanced at his watch. "We have about nine hours if they give us the time they promised."

"Their promises aren't worth a damn!" Brooks said.

"I'd like to circulate," Jerry said, ignoring him. "There's just a chance someone may have seen Chambrun somewhere. If Avilla is the outside contact for those men upstairs, then he may be around somewhere. And then I will plan an attack on Twenty-two B—if it comes to that."

"I can provide you with all the extra men you need," Guardino said.

"I don't want strangers stumbling around unfamiliar corridors, advertising their presence. If it comes to an attack, it will be my men, who have a chance of producing some surprise."

"You think they're so stupid they won't be thinking miles ahead of you, Dodd?" Inspector Brooks asked.

"Maybe I'm smarter than they—or you—think, Inspector," Jerry said.

"You gentlemen can talk us all to death!" Mrs. Haven said, quite casually. "I'm like Inspector Brooks. My primary concern is for one person—Pierre! Find him, Jerry. Please find him!"

Victoria Haven didn't have to plead with me to find Chambrun. He was all that mattered to me in the whole damn situation. I didn't care about revolutions in Central America or political prisoners. I really didn't care about the hostages in Twenty-two B. I scarcely knew Hilary Foster, the girl singer who'd been snatched. Sir George Brooks, Sheldon Tranter and Raul Ortiz were guests of the hotel whom I knew by sight and nothing more than that. Chambrun was the most important person in my life! It may sound a little florid to say that I loved him, but I did.

Jerry Dodd stopped by me as he was leaving. "Do what you can with that army of reporters," he said. "They'll be asking to see The Man. Don't tell them we don't know where he is. Just tell them he's got to sit tight here, waiting for a call from Twenty-two B. I don't want them spreading rumors that he's missing until we know, for sure, that he isn't missing of his own free will."

"You think that's possible?" I asked.

Jerry gave me a hard look. "No," he said. "But I don't want an army of irresponsible hoodlums looking for him."

I caught a glimpse of myself in the mirror on the office wall. I looked like a bum who'd been on a three-day drunk. Before I faced the press I had to improve on that.

My apartment is at the other end of the hall from Chambrun's office and as I headed for it I remembered for the first time in hours that I'd left a bruised and beaten-up Sally Mills there.

I let myself in, expecting that she'd call out to me when she heard the front door open. She didn't call out because she was gone. It wasn't until I'd showered and shaved and put on a fresh tropical worsted suit that I noticed the note propped up on my mantel.

Mark, dear:

I'm sorry you couldn't get back sooner. I've been listening to your radio. I have to do what I can to help Hilary Foster. I owe her.

See you around, lover,

Sally

All we needed was a romantic girl who didn't know what the whole score was adding to our troubles. Well, I couldn't raise a sweat over her now, much as I cared for her. I had to cool off the reporters and then get to the only thing that really mattered to me.

I left my place and walked across the hall to the door that opened onto the mezzanine gallery that circles the lobby. I looked down at what should have been a familiar world and saw something I couldn't have imagined. There were hundreds of people milling around, and dozens of blue-uniformed cops who looked strangely out of place. Bellhops were trying to help checking-out guests with their luggage, and not having much luck getting them through the mob and out onto the safety of the street. Purse snatchers and chain grabbers, Johnny Thacker had told me, were having a field day. I could see cops nabbing a few of them, but in fact the whole place looked out of control.

"I saw you go to your apartment to freshen up. Do you mind if I join you, Mark?" Lois Tranter had come up behind me.

"This is the safest place to stay," I said. "I've got to go down there."

"If Avilla's in that crowd I could spot him, sooner or later," Lois said. "Please let me stay with you, Mark."

"It's important that we find Avilla," I said. He could be part of the whole conspiracy to free the political prisoners, could be the mastermind behind the hostage taking, could know what had happened to Chambrun. "Did your father ever mention Avilla to you before that time in the Trapeze?" I asked her. "In addition to being his daughter, you're his personal secretary. Had Ricardo Avilla's name ever come up before?"

"I spent a lot of my growing up time with my father in Central America," Lois said. A look of pain twisted her movie-star face. "My mother died when I was only four years old. It was a flu epidemic. Father was away—in Guatemala, I think. Friends of his took care of me till he could get back, which was three or four days. They hadn't been able to find him to tell him about my mother. I—I was a problem to him. There was no immediate family, no brothers or sisters on either side, no aunts or uncles."

"A busy, active man left with a four-year-old child," I said.

She nodded. "I—I didn't really understand that at the time. I was in shock, having had it explained to me that my mother wouldn't be back from the hospital. It—it was my first encounter with death." She gave me a little smile. "I was only concerned about me, not my father."

"That's understandable." While she was talking I was watching the unruly mob that had taken over my world.

"The first night he was home I was put to bed while he had a conference with someone from Washington, one of his superiors. I crept down the hall and listened outside the living-room door. That—that's when I found out how much my father cared for me. He was telling his friend—or boss—that he was going to have to resign from his position and find work that would let him stay with me. The friend—or—boss—was urging him to find some other answer. Dad was vitally important down there in Central America. He was one of the few Americans who had friendly contacts on both sides of the perpetual revolutions that were going on. I didn't understand all that then, of course. What was going to happen to me was all that mattered. The friend kept urging him not to resign, and finally suggested that Dad must have some friend, a family down there somewhere, where I could stay, where he could see me every day. I was an exhausted little girl that night, but I listened and listened, until my father began to consider the possibility of taking me back with him. I wasn't to be deserted after all! I guess, when I felt safe, I fell asleep—right outside the living-room door. The next thing I knew, I was in my father's arms, being held very tenderly, and carried back to my room. There has never been a day of my life—until today—that I haven't shared some part of with him." Her hands were gripping the railing of the mezzanine gallery. "It's not possible to think of him, up there in that room with those monsters, his life hanging on a decision some stranger will make!"

"Let's get back to Ricardo Avilla," I said, after a moment of watching the knuckles on her hands turn white as she gripped the balcony railing. "Your father never mentioned him to you before he pointed him out to you night before last in the Trapeze?"

"The name Avilla is a familiar one in Central America," she said. "The Avillas are heroes or villains, depending on which side you talk with down there. They go 'way back, as you obviously know from Mrs. Haven. Carlos Avilla, Mrs. Haven's man, was a kind of national hero to the people on the left. Their George Washington! His sons were leaders on the left after him. The family where I grew up, an English engineer named Craven, used to talk about them. 'I wish we had their kind of fighter on our side,' Mr. Craven used to say."

"His side being the right?"

"The English side, the American side," Lois said.

"And Ricardo Avilla?"

Lois shook her head. "I don't think I ever heard him mentioned till my father pointed him out to me the other night."

"But your father suggested he was a major terrorist," I

said. "Tell me, your father must have records, papers, diaries which would contain information about a man he considered so important. You're his secretary. Are there documents of his you don't get to see?"

"I see what he wants to show me," Lois said.

"Where does he keep those documents?" I asked. "There could be something that might tell us where Ricardo Avilla could be staying in New York, who his friends are who might know."

She shook her head again. "Our visit to New York was to be a short one. We were due to head back in two or three days. He didn't bring records or files with him except those that might have to do with the peace negotiations the OAS is trying to get started."

"There's a chance," I said. "Would he have papers here in his hotel room?"

"A day-to-day diary, I think. That would just cover what's been happening since we got here."

"He might have seen Ricardo Avilla here in the hotel before your time in the Trapeze. There could be some comment about him."

"I could look, if you can arrange to get me into his room," Lois said.

"Should be simple," I said. "Now I've got to deal with the press before they get completely out of hand. So circulate. If you see Avilla, flag me down wherever I am."

When I got to the foot of the stairs leading into the lobby I was hit by what seemed like a tidal wave of people. Many of them were familiar. I deal with the press every day of the year, round the clock, and many of them were familiar. Strangers were, I assumed, special police reporters and feature writers who didn't ordinarily come our way. In ad-

dition to them were dozens and dozens of familiar faces,
regular guests of the hotel who used our bars, restaurants,
and other facilities. They knew me as the Beaumont's PR
man, who should have all the answers, and they were all
shouting their questions at me. All of them seemed to be
asking the same question in one form or another. "What are
you doing about the crisis on the twenty-second floor?"
There was no way an answer could be heard over the bed-
lam of questions.

I signaled to Jack Wilson, my International News friend.
"Pick out eight or ten people who can cover for your whole
army and bring them to my office. No way I can handle this
here."

Jack nodded and took off, and I headed back upstairs to
the second floor. My office is right next to my apartment,
down the hall from Chambrun's. My secretary wasn't
there, which was a sign of the general disorder.

I called Chambrun's office and Betsy Ruysdale answered. There was no news of Chambrun. There had been
no call from Twenty-two B.

"They're making out-calls, though," Betsy told me. "The
switchboard is taping them. Mr. Guardino's up there listening."

Then I remembered Lois Tranter. I asked Betsy to have
one of Jerry's men find Lois in the lobby and get her the
key to her father's room.

"And call me here in half an hour," I asked Betsy. "I'm
dealing with the press. Just tell me I'm needed and I'll
dump them. That's all the time I can give them."

For a moment or two, in the quiet of my office, I was
suddenly conscious of the almost unbearable fatigue I was
feeling. It wasn't only the lack of sleep and food, but the
anxiety that mounted with every passing minute, especially

since Chambrun had vanished from the scene. I was tempted by the bottle of Jack Daniel's I keep in my desk drawer, but I decided that even one drink might knock me on my behind. Chambrun wouldn't disappear without letting one of us know his intentions. He had been tricked, trapped, possibly even worse than that. Body in a trash can, Guardino had suggested. No, please God, not that!

Jack Wilson was a man I could trust, and he turned up with exactly ten of his fellow-journalists, most of whom I knew.

"I'm sorry I have to do it this way," I told them, "but I haven't got time to answer a thousand scattered questions."

"That's fair. We understand," Jack said. They waited for me to dish it out.

"We don't know much more than you already know," I said. "The hostages are still in Twenty-two B. We have until midnight to make the payoff they're demanding. We haven't heard from them in the last couple of hours. They're making out-calls which are being monitored but I haven't heard them so I can't tell you what they are."

"The political prisoners are being released?" Jack Wilson asked.

"As far as I know, they're being assembled at an airport in Georgia," I said.

"And will be flown to wherever they want to be taken?" someone asked.

"I assume so," I said. "But let me try to get you off my back by making something clear to you. No one connected with the Beaumont is making that decision. It will come from Washington and London and the Organization of American States. Our part in it, our instructions from the hostage takers, were to clear the twenty-second floor of guests, staff, the works—and keep anyone from invading that area. That we're doing and will continue to do. We have no part in any other decisions."

"But you're in cahoots with the police, the CIA, and God knows who else," Jack Wilson said. "You know what's going on whether you make decisions or not."

"We have an assistant to the police commissioner and a CIA man down the hall," I said. "But they aren't making decisions either. The decisions will come from much higher up."

"Is it possible the big shots will decide the hostages aren't worth saving?" one of the reporters asked.

"I can't tell you that," I said. "Obviously, someone on the outside is communicating with the people in Twenty-two B. They're getting information from you by way of radio and TV. The big shots are going through the motions of carrying out their demands. The political prisoners are being assembled in Georgia. What the last-minute decision will be I can't tell you. What Chambrun will do if we're left holding the bag I can't tell you. I don't think he knows himself."

"What do the police and the CIA say about a man named Ricardo Avilla?" Jack Wilson asked me.

That one surprised me. "Say about him?" I asked.

"A known Latin American terrorist, seen in the hotel. We understand he is a relative of a man who kidnapped your Mrs. Haven many years ago. We understand Sheldon Tranter pointed him out to his daughter a couple of nights ago."

"Where did you hear that?"

"From the daughter," Wilson said. "She's been looking for him ever since the hostages were taken."

"So you know as much as I do," I said.

"Are they trying to find him?" Wilson asked. "Could he be the person on the outside who's keeping the people in Twenty-two B informed?"

"Yes, they're trying to find him," I said. "Yes, he could be the person on the outside making reports to Twenty-two B."

"How?"

"Only a guess," I said. "Fancy radio equipment. No one's making in-calls on the telephone. They won't accept them."

"You have a description of him?"

"They're circulating a police artist's sketch drawn from Miss Tranter's information. A middle-aged Clark Gable with a tin hand."

"Will Chambrun try to rescue the hostages if the big shots foul out?" Wilson asked.

I wondered if he'd be able to do it.

I was, thankfully, alone for a moment, but only for a moment. Johnny Thacker stuck his blond head in my door. The day bell captain was showing the strain, like most of us.

"Two guys want to see you, Mark," he said. "I thought you'd want to see them."

"Who are they?"

"Max London, Hilary Foster's manager, and a young man named Roth who is Hilary's boyfriend. I have a feeling they might try something foolish, so I thought you ought to talk to them."

Max London is not a total stranger to me. A dark, wiry little man with heavy horn-rimmed glasses, he is one of the top talent agents in the business. We've had dealings with him quite often over the years, hiring entertainers for the Blue Lagoon night club.

"Thanks for seeing us, Mark," Max London said. "This is Bob Roth. He is engaged to be married to Hilary Foster."

Roth had close-cropped red hair and a face that looked like the map of Ireland. He had a look I was beginning to get used to around the Beaumont. He looked beat.

"We've been trying to get to Chambrun," Max said, "but he seems to have shut himself away."

"He has to stay undisturbed in case the people upstairs call him," I said, hoping it sounded true.

"Is there any news?" Roth asked. "I mean, about the hostages?"

"No," I said. "We have to hope they're all right, for the time being at least. There's still quite a little time, and so far we've done everything the hostage-takers have asked for."

"Hope?" Roth brought his fist down on the corner of my desk.

"Why do you think they took Hilary?" London asked.

"It's a guess," I said. "They wanted to be sure Chambrun did what they demanded of him. If you know Chambrun, you know that he would do anything to protect anyone who works for him."

"Bob doesn't think that's why they took her," London said.

"Why else?" I asked. "She's famous, of course. The general public would be concerned for her. That could bring pressure on people who have to make decisions."

"Tell him, Bob," Max London said.

"That bastard!" Roth said, and brought his fist down on my desk once more. He didn't seem to be able to talk, so London carried the ball.

110

"You know how it is with beautiful and talented women who appear in public," he said. "All kinds of men fall in love with them. They get gifts from strangers—flowers, perfume, expensive wines. Hilary had a guy like that pursuing her during the two weeks she's been playing here at the Beaumont. He came to the Blue Lagoon every night, brought her presents, tried to buy her drinks, make time with her."

"Bastard!" Roth almost shouted again.

"A girl in Hilary's position has to play it cool," London said. "She doesn't want to drive away a good customer from the place she's working."

"I don't know where this is getting us," I said.

"The guy who has been rushing Hilary," London said, "is Raul Ortiz."

That almost jarred me out of my chair. "But he's one of the hostages! Twenty-two B is his suite!"

"One of the hostages, my foot!" Roth said. "Everything we've heard says you don't know who's in charge up there. Well, think about it, Haskell! This Ortiz is no more a hostage than I am! His suite, everything prepared there for a big showdown. He never took Hilary to make an impression on Chambrun or the general public. He took her for himself. God knows what he's putting her through up there! Twenty-four hours of sexual brutality? That's what he wanted from her, wasn't it? So he takes her into a situation where no one dares lift a finger to help her. So help me God, if I ever lay hands on him . . . !"

"What do you know about Ortiz?" London asked me.

"What I know about all the guests in the hotel, which is almost nothing intimate," I said. "A guest registers and a card is filled out for him which we keep for reference purposes. Information like his home address, his credit rating, his business or political connections here in New York, his past record if he's been a guest before—is he an alcoholic, a drug user, a woman chaser? If he—or she—is someone very much in the public eye, like a movie star, some kind of diplomatic hotshot, their wishes about the press are noted. Do they want it known they are here or do they want to stay quiet, undercover? I see those cards every morning of my life, at the regular meeting with Chambrun and his secretary."

"Raul Ortiz? What about him?" Roth demanded.

"I don't remember," I said.

"Oh, great!"

"I don't remember because obviously there wasn't anything to remember," I said. "Good credit rating, no eccentricities worth noting. Nothing I *needed* to remember as public relations man for the hotel. Since last night I know a little more about him, but so do you. He's been written about, talked about by the media round the clock. Member of the peace commission meeting at the United Nations on Central America."

"What we've told you could be important," Max London said. "Ortiz may be an enemy and not a victim."

It could be, I thought, and Sam Yardley and Guardino—and Chambrun if he was available—should know. If Ortiz was a villain, that explained why his suite had been chosen as the place to hold hostages. He could have had days to prepare, stocking the place with food and liquor. There would have been time for careful placement of the bomb or bombs that could blow us to pieces. Communications with someone on the outside could have been set up and carefully tested before the planned raid took place that would keep us too busy to get in the way of the hostage-taking.

"If you think I'm going to sit around twiddling my

thumbs while that bastard plays his slimy games with Hilary, you've got another think coming," Roth said. "I want to know what's being planned, what's being done. If I'm not satisfied—"

"There are others in the same boat with you," I said. "Sir George Brooks's brother, Sheldon Tranter's daughter."

"And who's worrying about Ortiz?" Roth asked.

I tried to give him a sensible answer, though I wasn't sure I believed it myself. "He's a foreign diplomat," I said. "People concerned for him could be making their inquiries direct to Washington, or to the police commissioner himself, or at the United Nations."

"Anyone who really cared for him would be here," Roth said. "I'm here, the Brooks man is here, the Tranter girl is here. You don't just sit around and do nothing when someone you love is in the lion's den."

"Maybe you do," I said. "Maybe you leave the rescue to a lion tamer. I'll take you to a couple of them."

I led the two men down the hall to Chambrun's offices. I left them in the outer room with the secretary and went into The Man's private sanctum. It was much as I'd left it. Betsy was there, and Sam Yardley, and Guardino. They were waiting—for what? That was the name of the game, I guess—waiting. Guardino, who'd been up to the switchboard checking on the out-calls from Twenty-two B reported that the calls had been to the State Department in Washington and to Ten Downing Street in London, simply warnings that time was passing! If the prisoners were not on a plane flying out of Georgia by the deadline, the hostages would begin to get it, one by one. Inspector Brooks was gone.

I told them that Max London and Roth were in the outer office. "I didn't want to bring them in here for fear they'd guess that Chambrun was missing. Anything from Jerry Dodd?"

There had been nothing. Yardley and Guardino agreed to talk to Roth and Max London in the outer office.

Roth told his story, his voice unsteady with anger and anxiety. "You can only read what I'm telling you one way," he said. "Ortiz is running the show. Now you tell me what you're going to do about it! I'm not going to wait eight hours while Hilary is being brutalized."

"So if we plan to wait for eight hours, what do you propose to do about it, Mr. Roth?" Guardino asked.

"If you haven't got the guts to go up there and get Hilary out, I'm going!" Roth said.

Guardino looked almost sympathetic. "In the first place you can't get there, Mr. Roth," he said. "Stairways, back and front, blocked by hotel security and police. No elevators will stop at the twenty-second floor. And if you found some way to get there, we've been warned that any attempt to do that will result in the first hostage going out a window. The chances are you, too, would be shot down."

"So get me up there," Roth said. "While they're polishing me off in the front hall, you bring your people in the back way."

"You'd give up your life on the chance we'd succeed?" Guardino asked.

"You're darn right I would!"

I don't know about the others, but I believed he meant it. But I could hear Chambrun, if he'd been there, making some sardonic remark about heroics.

"Let me put in my two cents' worth, Mr. Roth," Sam Yardley said. The CIA man had a reassuring sound. "I know Raul Ortiz. I know him personally and professionally. You think it helps prove your theory that no one is concerned

114

about him—no one like you, or Inspector Brooks, or Lois Tranter. Let me assure you that there is great concern for Ortiz, most of it funneled to the CIA in Washington. At the top of my list of instructions is to do everything possible to get him out safely. You see, Ortiz is one of the Central Americans who is very much on our side down there. He has cooperated with us in a variety of covert activities. He would be a prime target for the people who are engineering this to get those prisoners free. We can't afford to have anything happen to Ortiz and they know it."

"And so you ignore his interest in Hilary?" Roth asked. "What good is she to them? They took her because this animal, Ortiz, wants her."

"He is a Latin. A beautiful and talented woman would get to him. He is also a man of great courage and daring. He would be tough to handle in a hostage situation. During twenty-four hours of waiting he might try your kind of heroics, Mr. Roth."

"So he promised to be a good boy if they'd provide him with Hilary?"

"It could be," Yardley said. "That Ortiz really cares for your lady."

"Bastard!" Roth exploded.

"It could be they took her to make certain that Ortiz didn't make any sort of move against them. He tries something and they destroy her, right in front of him. I think you should hope that he cares enough for her to stay quiet."

I thought I could see the courage and bravado draining away from Roth as though somebody had pulled the plug on it.

"You—you think that's the way it is?" he asked.

Yardley answered in his soft, level voice, "I think it could be that way. I think it's as good an explanation as yours, and

I have the advantage of knowing Ortiz, what he stands for, what this all adds up to for him."

"If you could have seen the way he went after Hilary," Roth said. "Flowers, gifts, even jewelry which she wouldn't take from him."

"Didn't she tell him about you?" I asked.

"Of course she did! He just laughed and said until the preacher spoke the magic words over us he was still in the running."

"He's a man who plays to win," Yardley said.

"Okay!" Roth's juices were beginning to flow again. "What are you people going to do?"

"People in high places all around the world are trying to come up with an answer," Yardley said. "I'm waiting for orders from my department, Guardino's waiting for orders from his." He glanced at me. "Chambrun's doing exactly what he's been told to do by the guys up in Twenty-two B. That's the only thing he can do for the hostages just now. Make sure nothing happens so that they have to show us they mean what they say."

"You mean harm one of the hostages?"

"That's what I mean, Mr. Roth."

Roth turned away and then back at Yardley. "You know what I'd do if I had the decision to make?" he asked.

"Sensible advice is in short supply around here," Yardley said.

"When I had those eight prisoners all assembled at that airport in Georgia, I'd take them all outside and stand them against a wall in front of a firing squad. In front of television cameras, so those bastards upstairs could see for themselves what's happening. Then I'd give them five minutes to set the hostages free, unharmed."

"And if they didn't?"

"I'd mow down their eight friends, right on camera for them," Roth said.

Yardley's smile was thin and tight. "If it's any comfort to you, Roth, that's an option that has been suggested to my people."

"Well, then?"

"One of the problems in the crises we face all around the world, Roth, is that the people of other nationalities and other political persuasions are not like us. Shoe on the other foot, and they could do exactly what you're suggesting. They know how different we are, though. They know we would never slaughter eight prisoners, legally held, in cold blood. They'd know we were bluffing."

"So we aren't bluffing!"

"I'm afraid we would be, Mr. Roth. Nobody would ever give the order for a firing squad to kill."

"So we knuckle under and lose the hostages along the way?"

"There must be some way to put the heat on them that they'll know we will and can carry out," Yardley said.

"Such as?"

"A lot of pretty good minds are working on that, Roth, and we still have some time in which to come up with an answer."

"But you don't have the answer?"

Yardley's mouth narrowed to a tight slit. "Not yet," he said.

Two hours had gone by since Chambrun had taken off for Mrs. Haven's penthouse on the roof and never made it. There was simply no explanation for why he could have stayed out of touch for so long voluntarily. It would be out of character, against his own rigid rules. No matter what kind of crisis he'd encountered, he wouldn't have left us hanging there, waiting to hear from him, if there was any way he could have avoided it.

Yardley had, I thought, put the brakes to any notions Bob Roth had had for single-handed heroics. I had got the press off our backs for at least a little while. And I hadn't the faintest idea of my next move.

Max London and Roth took off to sweat it out somewhere else. Yardley and Guardino and I went back into The Man's office where Betsy Ruysdale was holding the fort alone. I wondered what had happened to Mrs. Haven.

According to Betsy, the old lady had gone back up to her penthouse to prepare for her regular afternoon visit to the Trapeze Bar. Five o'clock was close at hand. Betsy smiled. "Mrs. Haven promises that, in spite of her vanity, she will wear her glasses! If there is anything to see, she will see it. Or anyone, like Ricardo Avilla."

Yardley and Guardino were both at phones, one at Chambrun's desk and the other in the dressing room adjoining the main office. I was alone with Betsy, and to my surprise she was suddenly standing close to me, her hands gripping my arms.

"I am so damn scared, Mark," she said. "Pierre would never . . ."

"I know."

Now her face was buried against my shoulder and she was fighting tears.

"He's a survivor," I said, trying to comfort her.

She leaned back and looked up at me. "You know why?" she asked. "Because he's never taken by surprise."

"What could have changed his mind after he started out to see Mrs. Haven?" I asked.

118

"A man with a gun in his back," she said, and lowered her head against my shoulder again.

Where and how could this have happened? He had been in the lobby, surrounded by a mob of people. The elevator operator he'd told to take a break for a cup of coffee had seen him about to take a car to the roof. He hadn't ever got to the roof. Our security up there was good and trustworthy. Had he stopped the car, for some reason, on the way up? He should have been seen if he'd gotten off the car at any floor. Since all this security had been hastily improvised, it was possible, only just possible, that he could have stopped at a floor somewhere and not been seen. Of course he could have stopped at Twenty-two, but that didn't make sense. He had every reason to believe that would be walking straight into disaster.

Mullins, the elevator man, hadn't actually seen him get on the car. What could have changed his mind? Had he seen some person or some action that he thought required his instant attention? Could someone stick a gun in his back in that mob of people and go unnoticed? I realized that of course that could happen. With people shoving and elbowing each other Chambrun would know, if he was suddenly threatened, felt a gun barrel stuck in his ribs, that he'd better obey the orders he was given or he could be shot dead and the killer would have an excellent chance of evaporating in the crowd.

But he hadn't been shot dead, not there in the lobby. Where could he have been taken without security spotting him? He was as well-known as a movie star to most of them.

I put an arm around Betsy to encourage her to get over her momentary crack-up. I knew that danger to Chambrun meant a great deal more to her than her boss-secretary relationship would occasion. They were very circumspect about whatever their real relationship was, but no one who knew them doubted for a minute that it was far more intimate than anything that had to do with work.

"He tells you things that he might not tell anyone else," I said to Betsy. "Was there anything before he left for Mrs. Haven's place that suggested he had some other project on his mind?"

Betsy shook her head. "He—he seemed to think that the attack on Mrs. Haven wasn't just a casual part of the raid on the hotel. Someone had gone after her very deliberately. He thought Mrs. Haven had seen something, or might see something, that was dangerous to the attackers."

I had one of the first bright ideas I'd had in the last few hours. "Sir George Brooks was one of the key people they wanted as a hostage," I suggested to Betsy. "Someone came up there to get him, and there was Lady Victoria sitting in her garden, out in the open. The attacker thought she might see him, could identify him."

"But she didn't see anyone!" Betsy said.

"I know. But she didn't have on her glasses! The attacker didn't know that she couldn't see anything ten feet away from her without them."

"'Remember to kill me,'" Betsy said.

"That was forty-five years ago, love," I said. "Anyone from back then would have had to be in a wheelchair."

"Mrs. Haven isn't in a wheelchair," Betsy said. "Neither is that Avilla man's grandson."

"I've got to find Ricardo Avilla, Betsy," I said.

"He isn't going to be anywhere around here, Mark. The security, the police—everyone is looking for him. They have his picture."

"If he's the outside contact for the people in Twenty-two B he's *got* to be around here," I said.

"What could he tell them that isn't on television?" Betsy asked. "He hasn't any way of knowing what Pierre is thinking, or Yardley, or Guardino. He can't know what Jerry Dodd may be thinking or planning. All he has to do is stay out of sight."

"There's a chance he can be hanging around," I said. "How could he know we're looking for him? I'm going to check out Lois Tranter. She's probably still circulating down in the lobby."

Betsy's fingers tightened on my arms. "Stay looking for Pierre, Mark. He's all that matters!"

"Locating Avilla may be the way to find him," I said.

I didn't go directly down to the lobby to check with Lois Tranter. As I was leaving the office I glanced at my watch and saw that it was nearly five-thirty. If Victoria Haven had carried out her plans, she would be across the mezzanine in the Trapeze Bar, holding court. Having come up with a new idea about the reason for someone shooting at her, I wanted to ask her about the incident again.

I walked across the mezzanine gallery toward the Trapeze. Nothing had changed down in the lobby. It was still a madhouse of people. The Trapeze is one of the favorite gathering places for the Beaumont's regular customers, particularly on an ordinary business day. It was a looked-forward-to stopover for men on the way home from work. Some years ago an artist of the Calder school had fashioned a collection of mobiles in the image of trapeze artists. These little figures moved gracefully in the breeze circulated by the air conditioning and had given the bar its name.

Mrs. Haven was at her usual corner table with Toto sit-

121

ting sullenly on his red satin cushion on the chair beside her. She was surrounded by eight or ten friends and admirers, who were flooding her with questions. After all, she was a key figure in the excitement of this day, having been marked for murder.

As I walked in the side door I found myself confronted by Mr. Del Greco, the captain.

"Oh, it's you, Mark," he said. "We're trying to keep the curious out of here and cater only to our regulars. Hell to pay, yes?"

"Yes," I said. "I see Mrs. Haven in here as usual."

"Queen of the ball," Del Greco said. "Some old lady!"

I looked across at the bar. Eddie Walsh, the head bartender, looked as though he'd just been through a Waring mixer. There was a patch of adhesive tape over his right eye. His left eye squinted through a beautiful purple shiner. I saw he had a bandage around his right forearm.

"What happened to Eddie?" I asked.

Del Greco's smile tightened. "Fighting off some of the bums who raided us last night," he said. "He was pretty badly beaten up and carted off to our emergency hospital. They thought he might have a concussion. Apparently not, and they just let him out. He insisted on coming back to work. Another star of the evening! It was hell in here for a while, Mark."

"I can imagine."

"Is there any inside dope on what's going on upstairs?"

"You know as much as I do if you've been watching TV," I said.

I made my way over to Mrs. Haven's table. She had promised to wear her glasses, but they were sitting on the table beside her. I was close enough to touch her before she recognized me.

122

"Mark! Welcome to our city. Any news?"

"Nothing that you don't know," I said. Obviously she hadn't told her friends that Chambrun was missing or I'd have been bombarded with questions. There was no way to talk to her privately, so I took it out in the open.

"There's a theory about why you were shot at," I told her, and outlined my idea.

"If you knew what was going on in the hotel, you'd have been expecting trouble, wouldn't you, Victoria?" one of her friends asked.

"But I didn't know what was going on in the hotel," she said. "It was all in the lobby on the lower floors. The noise didn't carry up to the roof. I didn't dream anything was happening till I heard the shot and felt the pain in my arm."

"You hear anyone come up to the roof?" I asked her. "The elevator?"

"I did hear the elevator door open and close," she said. "I didn't pay any attention, because I didn't know I should have paid any attention. I thought it was probably Pierre going to his place, or Sir George Brooks going to his."

"You didn't see anyone?"

She gave me a dazzling smile and pointed to her glasses.

"You weren't curious?"

"Why should I have been? Pierre comes and goes. Whoever's in Penthouse Three comes and goes. I don't keep tabs on them. After that first shot I was ducking for my life."

"Smart girl," somebody said.

That was that. I went over to the bar to talk to Eddie Walsh. "You bumped into a door, I take it," I said.

Eddie grinned at me. "You ought to see the other guy," he said.

"We're looking for someone you may know by sight," I said. "Fellow named Ricardo Avilla."

"Sure I know him. Nice-looking middle-aged guy with a tin hand. He's been a regular recently."

"Night before last he was here," I said.

"Oh brother, night before last is like ten years ago today," Eddie said.

"Sheldon Tranter and his daughter were here and saw Avilla at the bar."

"That beautiful chick is Tranter's daughter?" Eddie asked. "I thought he'd picked himself up something very special!"

"His daughter," I said.

"I remember seeing them together," Eddie said. "Night before last? I guess that was when it was. But Avilla wasn't here that night."

"The girl mentioned seeing him. Her father gave her a rundown on Avilla. Some kind of Central American terrorist."

"He's a fast man with a five-buck tip," Eddie said. "But he wasn't here night before last."

"How can you be sure? I mean, people coming and going, you busy."

"I know because I had a message for Avilla and he never turned up to get it."

"Message?"

"Just a phone number for him to call. I never saw him to give it to him."

"I guess, in the excitement, somebody remembered wrong," I said. "Could have been the night before that, I suppose."

"Avilla could have been here then," Eddie said. "But Tranter and that girl—his daughter you say—were only here the once, night before last." Eddie's grin widened. "You don't forget when you saw a sexy chick like that. Second time I saw her, but the other time wasn't in here."

"Where?"

"You're asking me the same questions Chambrun asked me," Eddie said.

"Chambrun? When?" I asked.

"Couple of hours or so ago. He came to the hospital to see me. Told me to go home and rest up. I told him I wouldn't miss what was going on around here for anything."

"Where did you see Lois Tranter before?"

"Like I told Chambrun, it was a couple of days before the raid. She was coming out of the Annex Building. I wondered at the time if she was staying there alone. That kind of a girl might be worth looking up in my spare time. But then I saw her with Tranter night before last, and not knowing she was his daughter, I figured the competition was a little too high-class for me. Tranter is a big shot with money!"

"You're sure she wasn't here some other time with Tranter when Avilla was here?"

"Look, Mark, you don't forget a girl like that when you see her."

"What did Chambrun say when you told him this?" I asked.

"He said it was interesting," Eddie said.

"How did he happen to come to see you? He was supposed to be heading up to the roof to see Mrs. Haven."

"He told me that," Eddie said. "He was just starting up, he told me, when he ran into Mike Maggio. Mike told him I was in the hospital and, being the kind of guy he is, he came to see me."

"You got that phone number someone left for Avilla?"

"I gave it to Chambrun," Eddie said.

"You remember it?"

"Hell, no, Mark! I had it written on a piece of paper in my wallet. I gave it to The Man. Is something wrong with Chambrun? Jerry Dodd was just here asking if I'd seen him."

I hesitated. "He's been out of touch for a couple of hours," I said. "We've been wondering what he's up to. You tell Jerry what you've just been telling me?"

"No reason to. He didn't ask. What does it mean?"

"I wish I knew," I said. "One more question, Eddie. What is your off day?"

"Sundays," Eddie said. "That's our light night. Joe Bassilio takes over for me on Sundays."

"That could have been when Tranter and his daughter saw Avilla here."

"Five days ago is not night before last," Eddie said.

Lois Tranter had been very specific about when it was she and her father had seen Ricardo Avilla in the Trapeze. Night before last she had told us, and Eddie Walsh now agreed that she and her father had been there, but not Avilla. Somebody, in view of the upheaval in the Beaumont, could have been confused about the day. But I found it difficult to put that confusion on Eddie Walsh. He is a sharp, observant, totally reliable guy in my book. He had reason to remember that Avilla hadn't been in the Trapeze night before last. "A fast man with a five-buck tip" isn't easily forgotten, especially when you have a message for him that would probably produce another five-buck tip.

Lois had been very certain about when she and her father had seen Avilla in the bar. She hadn't said "a few days ago." It was night before last, and yet Eddie had reason to be certain it hadn't been. Lois had been there with her father, but not Avilla. I tried to make it work out so that both sides were telling the truth. Lois hadn't known Avilla by sight; he was pointed out to her by her father. How well did Sheldon Tranter know Ricardo Avilla? He could know Avilla's history and not know the man well by sight. He could have seen him in some large gathering in Central America, known that he was presently in New York, seen someone he *thought* was Avilla and delivered his speech about Avilla to his daughter. It could be that both Lois and Eddie Walsh were telling the exact truth as they knew it.

What didn't make sense to me was that Eddie had seen Lois, some days ago, coming out of the Annex Building, which is next door to the Beaumont. Some years ago when extensive alterations were taking place in the hotel, the Beaumont Corporation had bought an old brownstone house next door to the hotel and moved some of the business-office functions there. When that time was over, they had remodeled four apartments on the four floors of the brownstone for overflow use. They were rarely used because there was no way to supply room service or bar service to them. On rare occasions when there were big doings at the United Nations or some convention in the city, the hotel let the space be occupied. I wasn't aware that it was in use at the moment, certainly not by someone who had been called to my attention as a VIP. Sheldon Tranter had had a room in the hotel. There was no ready explanation for Lois's coming out of the Annex. She would probably have one, and another that would clear up the confusion about the "night before last" in the Trapeze.

I went looking for her.

It seemed to me when I reached the lobby level that the

crowd had thinned a little. I think the rush of guests to check out had subsided. I saw Lois Tranter standing at the far end, and started toward her. She made a gesture to me, waving a hand across her face, to indicate that she hadn't seen Avilla anywhere.

I changed my mind and headed for the front desk. Atterbury, the head clerk there, looked out on his feet.

"Like to ask you a question," I said.

Atterbury gave me a deadpan look. "Don't ask me what day it is, or what time it is, or what my name is," he said.

"Rough going?" I asked.

"Rough is a minor-league word for it," he said.

"I need to know if anybody is staying in the Annex," I said.

"Not registered in—that I know of," Atterbury said.

"A few days ago?"

"Some people from one of the Central American countries had the ground-floor apartment for a couple of days. We moved them back in here when we had room. It's empty at the moment."

"Some particular Central American?" I asked.

Atterbury shrugged. "Not on the registry book," he said. "A delegation to the UN needed office space. Some kind of peace conference business. Chambrun okayed letting them have an Annex apartment. Raul Ortiz, in Twenty-two B, was to be billed for it." Atterbury looked suddenly stunned. "He's one of the hostages, isn't he?"

"He sure as hell is," I said.

"Well, anyway, they used the space for a few days, and then we moved 'em into one of the private meeting rooms in here." He gestured toward the far end of the lobby. "You want a name for them?"

I did. Atterbury went to the registry and came back with

it. "Organization of American States," he told me. "Man in charge is one Luis Sanchez."

"Thanks," I said.

"Meeting Room Number Four," Atterbury told me.

I felt a little treacherous not going to Lois Tranter for answers, but I remembered an old adage of Chambrun's: "Don't start asking someone questions unless you're equipped to tell a lie from the truth."

There are six private meeting rooms off the south end of the lobby. They are used for business meetings, private luncheons, or dinners. They are almost always in use. When I reached the door of Number Four I found it locked. I knocked and waited. After a moment the lock clicked and the door was opened a few inches. I found myself facing a dark-skinned young man who was pointing a handgun right at my chest. I don't remember anyone pointing a gun at me before. It's not a pleasant experience.

"Yes?" the young man asked.

"I'm Mark Haskell, public relations man for the hotel. I'd like to talk with Mr. Sanchez."

"Wait, please." The door closed, the lock clicked.

After a moment or two the door opened again and I was faced by a pleasant-looking middle-aged man with a white, toothpaste-ad smile.

"Come in, Mr. Haskell. I know you by sight, you see. I am Luis Sanchez."

There were four other men in addition to the young fellow with the handgun sitting down on one side of a sort of board-of-directors table. Two girls sat facing them, apparently secretaries, each with a phone jacked in front of her.

"Your friend surprised me," I said, nodding toward the young guy with the gun.

"You know what it's been like down here, Mr. Haskell?" Sanchez asked. He spoke good colloquial English with a slight foreign lilt to it. "People barging in who have no business with us—just curious. With our head man held hostage upstairs, we're not taking chances."

"Raul Ortiz?"

Sanchez nodded. "I dream you may have something hopeful to tell us."

"We're hopeful as long as we know our government and others are coming up with an answer," I said.

"They are dealing with madmen," Sanchez said. "You had a particular reason for coming here?"

"Your business here in New York, Mr. Sanchez?"

His white smile widened. "Rather ironic, isn't it? We are here on a peace mission. We find ourselves in the center of a terror game."

"Do you have any dealings with Sheldon Tranter?" I asked.

"Very close dealings," Sanchez said, "which is why he is being held hostage along with Ortiz and the others."

"You were quartered in the Annex Building next door earlier in the week?"

"Yes. They had no space for us in this main building when we first came here. Your Mr. Chambrun allotted us space next door until we were able to take over this room."

"You're living here in the hotel?"

"I have a room up on the seventeenth floor," Sanchez said. "The rest of my staff are scattered around town. Are you able to tell me that your government and the others involved are planning to meet the demands that have been made, releasing the prisoners they are holding?"

"I can only tell you that those prisoners are being assembled at an airport in Georgia. We still have some hours to complete that part of the demands that have been made."

"And they'll be flown to safety?"

"I can't answer that question, Mr. Sanchez. The powers involved will obviously be prepared to do that if they believe the hostages will be released."

"You think they will be?"

"I can tell you there are some doubts," I said.

"Because they can identify their captors?"

"What do you think?"

"I have wondered," Sanchez said. The white smile was frozen. "Ortiz has to be saved! Without him the whole bid for peace could crumble."

I got to where I wanted to go. "You have dealings with Sheldon Tranter?"

"But of course! He is our American contact."

"You know his daughter?"

"I don't think so," Sanchez said.

"She grew up in Central America, lived with him there, is now his secretary."

Sanchez's eyes brightened. "Very beautiful young woman? I didn't realize she was his daughter. I've seen her only once, I think."

"When was that?"

"A few days ago, when we were still in the Annex Building. She delivered some documents to us from Tranter." He glanced at the two rather plain girls sitting at the telephones and chuckled. "I remember thinking, when I saw Tranter's secretary, that you Americans have a genius for mixing business with pleasure."

"His daughter," I said.

"Well, then some other man must be very lucky," Sanchez said.

I felt better. There was nothing mysterious about Lois Tranter's being seen by Eddie Walsh coming out of the Annex. It had been a normal business activity for Tranter's secretary.

"Can you keep us informed on how things are developing, Mr. Haskell?" Sanchez asked.

"When I know anything," I said. "And you, if you hear anything that can be helpful, call the hotel switchboard and tell them you have something for me. God knows where I'll be, but the switchboard will know how to find me."

Sanchez's smile was gone. "If, in the end, you plan to attempt a rescue, know that you can count on the meager manpower I have here." He gestured toward the other men in the room.

"If it comes to that, Mr. Sanchez, we'll have skilled professionals to handle it."

The ghost of his smile returned. "I and my men here are not strangers to violence," he said. "Our part of the world nourishes violence."

I was at the door when I realized I hadn't asked him about Hilary Foster. "From all accounts Raul Ortiz was giving her quite a rush," I said, when I'd asked if he knew her.

Sanchez seemed to hesitate. "I don't think it is a new friendship," he said. "Miss Foster has appeared in Washington, where Raul has spent a lot of the last year. She has also toured South America and Raul first met her there. He was stationed in Brazil for a while."

"We couldn't understand why she was chosen to be a hostage at first," I said. "We thought it could be because she was appearing here at the Beaumont and Pierre Chambrun would go pretty far to protect anyone working for him. Then we decided your Señor Ortiz was the villain in

132

the piece, and had taken her hostage in order to satisfy his sexual appetites."

"What a bizarre notion!" Sanchez said.

"Then we thought she'd been taken to prevent Ortiz from trying anything reckless."

"That is possible," Sanchez said.

"Can there be another reason?" I asked. "Can she have gotten herself involved in the political mess in your part of the world?"

Sanchez looked like a man who was asking himself a question. "God knows, anyone who spends time down there has an impulse to take sides," he said. "She might have been carrying messages for Raul."

"Sir George Brooks?" I asked.

"Sheldon Tranter's opposite number in Great Britain," Sanchez said.

"So all four hostages could be working on the same side of the fence," I said.

"Certainly Raul and Sir George and Sheldon Tranter. Miss Foster, if she's been working for Raul."

"One more question and I'll be off," I said. "Do you know a man named Ricardo Avilla?"

Sanchez gave me a bitter little laugh. "Everyone in my part of the world knows the name Avilla," he said. "They have been part of our history for the last fifty, sixty years."

"Did you know that this Ricardo Avilla is here, has been a customer in the Trapeze Bar for some time?"

"Yes, I knew that," Sanchez said.

"And you haven't told the police or security?"

"Why should I?" Sanchez said.

"Doesn't it occur to you that he's working on the outside for the people who are holding the hostages?"

Sanchez drew a deep breath, as though he was suddenly

tired. "You don't know my world or our history, do you, Mr. Haskell?"

"I'm afraid not," I said.

"Guatemala, El Salvador, the rest of us are all alike," he said. There was a sudden bitterness in his voice. "Governments of the rich and powerful take charge, they talk a great democratic ball game, but the peasants, the farmers, the people, are trampled on. There have been rebellions down through the years, governments overthrown. Then the new men in power become rich, control the resources, get financial and technical help from your government, and walk on the people all over again. Way back, the Avillas led revolutions, but they were never able to get honest governments in place when they won. Today the revolutions are financed and supported by the communist world. The communists want to win so that they will have a foothold in your backyard. If they win, the people will be no better off than they have been under their own villains."

"Interesting, but this man Ricardo Avilla, helping them, would be in a powerful position, wouldn't he?"

"You don't know the Avillas," Sanchez said. "They have always really cared about the people. Ricardo Avilla hates the communists as much as he hates the very rich Americans who feed off us."

"You don't think he's involved with what's happened here?"

"If he is, then he'd be siding with the communists, and I would never believe that."

"You say you knew he was here and it hasn't disturbed you?" I asked. "Night before last, Tranter saw him in the Trapeze Bar and gave his daughter a rundown on him— terrorist, villain of the first order."

"That surprises me," Sanchez said. "Terrorist, yes. But

his acts of terror have been aimed at the enemies of the people. I knew he was here, I thought because he was concerned with the peace negotiations we're here to work on. I've seen him, I've talked with him briefly, I—I know where he's living."

"Where?"

"In the Plaza Hotel at the south end of the park. He's been seen here because so many people involved with the negotiations are here. You're wasting your time if you think he's involved with the hostage situation. He's on the other side, always has been."

I found myself wondering if I was being sold a bill of goods or if Sanchez was leveling with me. How did I know which side he was really on? Who could be trusted from his cockeyed world?

I suppose I would insist with my last breath that I have no racial or religious prejudices against any man, but I'm afraid I'm infected with a familiar American disease. I'm not sure I can trust foreigners. Luis Sanchez could be staunchly on our side, and yet his perpetual smile and the faintly alien sound of his speech left me uncertain about him. He could be trying to protect Ricardo Avilla, trying to persuade me to look somewhere else. Sheldon Tranter was one of "us," and he'd made it clear to his daughter that Avilla was "the enemy."

I went looking for Lois.

She was where I'd last seen her, standing in a far corner of the lobby, watching, watching.

"I'm certain Avilla hasn't been here this afternoon," she said, as I joined her.

I looked at her and thought we ought to keep her as a permanent decoration for the lobby. Concern for her father, what must be the kind of fatigue that was eating at so many of us, did nothing to reduce the kind of electric excitement her beauty created. I saw some people starting to bear down on me. I was supposed to be a source of information for anyone who wanted to know what was going on in the Beaumont. I guided Lois to the little office back of the front desk where we could talk without interruption.

"Anything on Mr. Chambrun?" she asked me.

"A little," I said. "I want to pass it on to Jerry Dodd when I can find him." I told her that I now knew that Chambrun had stopped at our hospital facilities on the fourth floor to see Eddie Walsh, who'd been injured in the raid. Where he'd gone after he'd visited Eddie I didn't yet know. "Something Eddie told him changed his plans."

"Do you know what it was?"

I tried to make it sound casual. "Among other things, he says he saw you coming out of the Annex the other day."

She gave me a blank look. "The Annex?"

"Building next door to the hotel we use for overflow of guests."

"Oh."

"Luis Sanchez just told me you were there one day delivering some documents from your father. Sanchez and his staff were using the Annex for a couple of days."

"Oh, *that* building," she said.

"You know Sanchez?"

"I know who he is. He's part of the peace delegation that's working for the OAS. Important man in Central America."

"But you don't know him personally? He obviously has dealings with your father."

"I knew about him, of course," Lois said, "but I'd never

met him until that day I delivered a folder of papers to that building for Dad."

"So you don't have a personal opinion about him?"

"Mark, I don't understand what you're trying to get at."

"Sanchez has quite a different opinion about Ricardo Avilla than your father," I said. I told her what Sanchez's rundown on "the man with the tin hand" had been. "He doesn't believe Avilla is involved with the hostage situation here. He even told me where Avilla is staying in town."

"Where?"

"The Plaza Hotel."

"Well, so he and Dad have different opinions about Avilla. That happens, you know. Everything is so complex in that world, Mark. Different people get different stories, draw different conclusions. My father has no doubts about Avilla, and I don't think anyone knows the story in Central America better than he does. He's spent the last twenty years of his life there."

Then I played my ace. "Eddie Walsh says the night you say your father pointed out Avilla to you Avilla wasn't there."

She was sitting in a Windsor armchair and I saw her grip the arms. "He's mistaken, of course. Avilla was at the bar, Dad pointed him out to me and told me about him."

"Eddie has a reason for being sure Avilla wasn't there," I said. "He remembers you and your father being there." I smiled at her, trying to relax her. "You lit quite a fire under Eddie. He saw you coming out of the Annex a couple of days before, saw you again. Decided you were your father's girlfriend and threw in his towel."

"That's not funny, Mark. Dad and I were there. He pointed out Avilla. I was able to describe him to that police artist. Mrs. Haven recognized him from the drawing. It was Avilla."

"Eddie had gotten to know him," I said. "He was a good tipper and Eddie paid special attention to him. That night he had a message for him. Avilla never turned up so he could deliver it to him."

"Your Eddie could have been busy, missed him for the few minutes he was there. And—and it could have been a different night and he's confused about it."

"You said that was your first visit to the Trapeze. I tell you, love, Eddie would have remembered you if he'd seen you some other time. You are easily remembered!"

"I can't explain it, Mark. My father pointed out a man to me. I was able to describe him to the police artist. Mrs. Haven recognized him as Avilla."

"How well did your father know Avilla?" I asked. "Could he have made a mistake?"

"A double?" She shook her head. "Has your man Eddie seen the drawing the police artist made? Has Luis Sanchez seen it? Inspector Brooks recognized it and pointed out the fact that he wouldn't have been holding the drink in his crippled right hand. You trust your friend Eddie, but he's mistaken. I don't know how long Avilla was there in the bar—two or three minutes while my father talked about him. Your Eddie could have been involved with other customers, left the bar for a little while for some reason. Avilla was there!"

"Your father couldn't have been mistaken?"

"For God's sake, Mark, we can't ask him, can we?"

On an ordinary day Chambrun's office is the center of all activity. "When I don't know what's going on everywhere in my hotel, it will be time for me to retire," I've heard

138

Chambrun say. Everyone reported to him anything unusual that might be happening from roof to basement. Today the Beaumont was like a great ocean liner, adrift at sea with no one at the helm. Jerry Dodd, the security chief, was off on his own. Security people were away from their regular posts, assigned to cover stairways and corridors, aided by cops, to keep strangers from filtering into places where they had no business. The threat of a bombing didn't seem to discourage the curious. It was the old "it can't happen to me" theory. Famous last words, I thought.

I had managed to gather some odds and ends of conflicting evidence from Eddie Walsh, Lois Tranter and Luis Sanchez. Jerry Dodd was the one person, with Chambrun missing, with whom I wanted to share what I had. Somehow Yardley, the CIA man, and Guardino, the cop, didn't inspire my confidence. If Jerry wanted their help, it was his decision to make. I had to find him.

He hadn't checked back into the office when I went back there. Betsy Ruysdale was there with Guardino and Yardley, waiting for what? I noticed a stack of copies of the police artist's drawing of the man we assumed was Ricardo Avilla on the table opposite Chambrun's desk. I took one of them and headed out across the mezzanine to the Trapeze again. I showed the drawing to Eddie Walsh.

"That's Avilla," he said without hesitation.

"Drawn from a description Lois Tranter gave the police artist," I said. "The man she saw here at the bar night before last when she was here with her father."

"Like I told you, Avilla wasn't here that night," Eddie said. "She saw him somewhere, but not here."

"If he just stopped for one drink, you can have been busy," I said. "You could have gone to the john for a few minutes."

"I don't have to go to the john when I'm on duty," Eddie said. He grinned at me. "I prepare in advance. And I'm never too busy to miss seeing a guy who might slip me a five-buck tip. Avilla wasn't here that night, Mark. That's for sure. Again, I had a message for him; I was looking for him to show. He didn't show while Tranter and his daughter were here, nor any other time that night."

"You still don't remember the telephone number you had to give him?"

"I'm sorry, Mark. I wrote it down, gave it to Chambrun. That's that."

I went down to the lobby level and along the back corridor to the private room where Luis Sanchez and his staff were holed up. Once again I was confronted by the young man with the gun, and once again I felt a cramp in my stomach muscles. I hoped he didn't have an itchy finger. But he summoned Sanchez and once again I was admitted. The same staff of people, as far as I could tell, were sitting around the directors' table—waiting like the rest of us, for what?

I showed Sanchez the drawing. "That's Ricardo Avilla, without any question," he said. "He has a little scar near his left eye, but the Tranter girl wouldn't have noticed that across a room."

"You still say you don't think he's part of what's going on here?" I asked.

"He hates the communist guerrillas," Sanchez said. "No way. I'd bet my life on that, Mr. Haskell."

Doubts, doubts, doubts. Sanchez *could* be trying to get us to look some other direction. I thanked him and left. Then I had some luck. In the corridor outside I ran head-on into Jerry Dodd.

"Boy, am I glad to see you! Anything?"

Jerry, his face frozen, shook his head. "Not a trace of him," he said.

I told him I'd come up with part of the trail. He'd been told that Eddie Walsh was in the hospital on four and gone there to see him. He'd asked Eddie about Avilla and gotten his story. Eddie had seen Lois Tranter come out of the Annex a couple of days before, seen her again in the Trapeze when she said she'd been there with her father, but no Avilla.

"I've just shown Eddie this drawing and he still says Avilla wasn't there," I said. "Just now Luis Sanchez confirms that the drawing is of Avilla, but he's certain he isn't involved with the people in Twenty-two B. Wrong politics, or what have you."

Jerry stood for a moment, tugging at his lower lip. "There's a coincidence in all that," he said. "The Man was in the hospital on the fourth floor. He gets Eddie's story about seeing Miss Tranter come out of the Annex."

"Delivering papers for her father," I said. "I checked that with Sanchez—and her."

"But Eddie didn't know that and neither did The Man. From the service area on the fourth floor there's a catwalk over to the roof of the Annex. It's used by the cleaning people and the trash collectors so they don't have to go out on the street to get in."

"I've been working here more than ten years and I didn't know that," I said.

"The Man knew, of course. He could have used it to go over there."

"Why? There's no one there. He'd know that, too."

"Eddie had called it to his attention. He was right there."

"And stayed there for all this time?" I asked.

"He could have had a fall, hurt himself, something. Let's have a look, Mark."

We took an elevator to four and walked across the little catwalk to the roof of the Annex. The door from the house to the roof was unlocked and we went down into the building. There was, as we knew, no one in the building and it was dead quiet.

The top three apartments were neatly prepared for guests in case there should be an overflow.

We walked into the living room of the ground-floor apartment, and there was Chambrun! He was handcuffed to a pillar that supported the ceiling in a far corner of the room, a wide strip of adhesive tape fastened over his mouth.

Jerry reached him first, peeled off the adhesive strip. The hanging judge was staring at us. "It took you long enough," Chambrun said. "You can't bite off those handcuffs with your teeth. You'll have to get a metal saw somewhere."

"Are you okay, Boss?" Jerry asked.

"Do I look okay?" Chambrun asked. "Well, don't just stand there!"

The reunion in Chambrun's office was almost like a party for a few minutes. Chambrun was swarmed over by all of us. The first person to reach him when he walked into the office was Betsy Ruysdale. There was just a touch of hands, but I could see she was fighting the impulse to throw her arms around him. Their personal feelings would have to wait. Guardino and Yardley were there; Dr. Partridge, the house physician, had been summoned. It turned out that Chambrun had been slugged and there was a lump on the back of his head the size of an egg.

He managed, after a rush of greetings, to tell us what had happened. Mike Maggio had stopped him as he was starting up to see Mrs. Haven on the roof and told him that Eddie Walsh had been hurt and was in the hospital on the fourth floor. Eddie is one of Chambrun's favorites on the hotel staff and he decided to stop on the way up to see how he was. Eddie was preparing to go back to work and couldn't be dissuaded. Chambrun, remembering Lois Tranter's story, asked Eddie about Ricardo Avilla and got the answer we had. Avilla hadn't been there. Eddie's remembering that he'd seen Lois coming out of the Annex a few days back roused Chambrun's curiosity. He would take the time to cross over to the Annex and see what there was to see—if anything.

He'd found things, as we had, neatly prepared for the next tenant, when and if. As he was walking down from the third floor he heard voices from below. He knew the Annex wasn't occupied at the moment. There shouldn't be anyone there.

"Men's voices," Chambrun told us, "speaking in Spanish. My Spanish isn't fluent, and they were speaking rapidly, as if they were talking on the telephone. I couldn't follow what was being said. I moved down as quietly as I could. The door to the ground-floor apartment was standing ajar and I looked in. One man was sitting at the table there with some kind of radio gadget in front of him. The second voice was someone being received by him from somewhere else. This was it, I thought, the outside contact with the people in Twenty-two B. I was a damn fool not to be alerted by the fact that the apartment door was standing open. I should have known someone else was around. Before the man at the radio saw me, I was slugged from behind, knocked cold."

"Lucky you don't have a concussion," Dr. Partridge said.

"Always had a hard head, Doctor," Chambrun said. "When I came to I was chained to that post—handcuffs, I guessed—and my mouth taped over. The two men were packing up their radio gear. They never spoke to me. They just left. There was nothing I could do to get free. I could just hope someone might have occasion to come into the Annex for something. So—catch me up?"

"First, you'd know those two men if you saw them again?" Guardino asked.

"I'd like to think they were photographed on my mind," Chambrun said. "Dark, Hispanic types. I might or might not be able to pick them out of a lineup. I don't have a good-enough ear for Spanish to pick out anything from their speech patterns."

The red light on Chambrun's telephone began to blink. The switchboard wouldn't put through a call that wasn't important. Betsy Ruysdale answered. She stood there, pointing toward the ceiling. It was a call from Twenty-two B.

Chambrun switched on the squawk box and answered.

The voice that came through the box had a kind of sardonic humor to it. "Welcome home, Mr. Chambrun," the man said. He knew! "Sorry, but no questions about your adventure. I warned you, Mr. Chambrun, that any attempt at heroics would cost lives. I am sending you a present on the service elevator. When you take the lid off the trash can it carries, you will find that I was not joking."

Chambrun's voice was ice-cold. "One of the hostages?"

"Too bad you have to learn the hard way," the voice said, and the connection was broken.

Jerry Dodd was instantly on the phone to one of his men somewhere, presumably in the basement garage. Cham-

144

brun was already on the move, with Doc Partridge and me at his heels. I suppose Guardino and Yardley and the others followed. Could it be Hilary Foster, or Tranter, or Sir George Brooks, or Raul Ortiz?

It was easier to run down the two flights of stairs to the basement than wait for an elevator. When we got there, several cops and one of Jerry's security men were standing around the service elevator from the west side of the hotel. One of them had taken the lid off a metal trash can in the car.

No one spoke, but they made way for Chambrun. I was right behind him. There was a body in the can—the body of a man. Thank God it wasn't Hilary Foster, I thought. Then I saw that it was Inspector Brooks. His eyes were rolled up in his head and he'd been shot squarely in the middle of the forehead.

"Crazy bastard tried to pull a rescue on his own," I heard Chambrun say.

I felt a little sick to my stomach.

PART
THREE

1

So now we had a murder on our hands and it changed things in a radical way. The police had been with us for hours since the raid, but we had been running our own show. Now Guardino was in charge of this one detail of our problem. Somehow, though, the good Lord has a way of smiling on Chambrun. The homicide chief for our particular district was Lieutenant Walter Hardy, an old friend who had been involved with our troubles before. He and Chambrun could work together without hostility, they could listen to each other and neither of them be Mr. Know-it-all.

When Hardy appeared in Chambrun's office after our grim discovery in the basement I felt some of my tensions relax. We had a winning team together again.

"This isn't our usual kind of case, Walter," Chambrun said, his voice bitter. "We know who the victim is. We know why he was killed. We know who killed him. We know where the killer is. And our hands are tied. You can't go up there and take them without risking four other lives."

Hardy is a big, blond man who looks more like a slightly befuddled fullback than a sometimes-brilliant crime fighter. He takes it slow and easy and stays with it no matter how long it takes.

"I've started my kind of slow approach, Pierre. It seems this Inspector Brooks used police authority to get the keys to his brother's penthouse. I should have thought your man Atterbury would have known that Scotland Yard doesn't have any authority here."

"I would have gotten him the keys if he'd asked me for them," Chambrun said. "He was assigned by the British government to come here to help his brother. He had the right to see his brother's possessions, papers, whatever."

Hardy shrugged. "He did go up to Penthouse Three, it seems. Your security people up there saw him, questioned him, were satisfied that he had a right to go in. He stayed there nearly an hour, they say. Your switchboard says he made a call to London while he was there."

"You know who he called?" Guardino, who was listening, asked.

"Lord Huntingdon, chief of British Security. I have a man trying to check with him. Past eleven o'clock over there. The number Brooks called is Huntingdon's office. We're trying to find a home number for him."

"Twenty-two B has also been calling Huntingdon," Chambrun said. "I doubt you'll find him at home. He'll be wherever they're discussing what the final decision is to be about the prisoners at that Georgia airport."

"We'll find him," Hardy said. "Anyway, after an hour, Brooks left Penthouse Three. He spoke to your security people up there. Said he'd found what he wanted. They say he was carrying a manila envelope with him that probably contained papers. He took the front elevator, not the service elevator where you eventually found him. Your people had no responsibility except to make sure he'd gone and they knew exactly who was on the roof—only Mrs. Haven at that time. She went down shortly afterwards—going to the Trapeze for a drink, she told them."

"She did," I said. "I saw her there."

"Doesn't matter," Hardy said. "Point is, nobody watched the elevator indicator to see where Brooks went."

"Why should they?" Chambrun asked. "He was legitimate, on legitimate business."

"No reason," Hardy said. "It would have been nice, that's all."

"We know where he went," Chambrun said. "To the twenty-second floor."

"Why? He knew how dangerous it was. He'd been warned, along with all of you."

"Perhaps he just didn't believe they'd shoot him in cold blood when he stepped off the elevator," Guardino said.

"We don't know that happened," Hardy said.

"Why would he risk going there?" Guardino asked.

"Maybe he found something in his brother's papers he thought he could trade for him," Yardley said.

"And it wasn't good enough?" Hardy asked.

"Unless you know terrorists, you can't believe they'll do what they do," Chambrun said. "I was there once."

I knew he was referring to what he called "the dark days," the Nazi occupation of Paris when he was a very young man.

"He believed they'd talk to him, and that he had something to sell," the CIA man said. "You have to know them to understand how totally cold-blooded they can be. Knowing them is why we've been sitting around here for hours doing nothing."

"What are you thinking of doing?" Hardy asked.

"We don't have an answer yet from higher up," Yardley said.

"And only a few hours for that answer to come," Hardy said. "Well, it's not quite as cut-and-dried as you put it, Pierre. Yes, we know who the victim is. We *think* we know

151

why he was killed, simply that he turned up there. It could be something he found out when he got there and talked to them. We know who the hostages are, but we don't know who 'they' are, the people holding them."

"We know who 'they' represent," Yardley said.

"That's not good enough for me," Hardy said. "I want the man who pulled the trigger. So, now I'd like to catch up on you, Pierre. They knocked you out, had you trussed up. Why did you go there?"

"Impulse," Chambrun said.

"Impulses will be the death of you some day, friend," Hardy said.

"Somebody working on the outside, communicating with the people up in Twenty-two B," Chambrun said. "Eddie Walsh told me about seeing Lois Tranter come out of there some days ago. I remembered that the Sanchez delegation had been assigned there for a couple of days."

"You don't trust them?"

"Right now I don't trust anyone who has a Hispanic sound to him. I was there on the fourth floor. I thought I'd take a look."

"And got clobbered for your pains."

"But my impulse was right," Chambrun said. "They were using the Annex as a base for communicating with Twenty-two B."

"You said you don't understand Spanish. How do you know they were communicating with Twenty-two B? Could be some whole other ball game, couldn't it? You just happened to stumble in on it."

"You don't believe that, Walter. Coincidences like that don't happen."

"Maybe—maybe not."

"There's one other thing Eddie Walsh told me that I've

let drop in all that's been happening," Chambrun said. "The night Lois Tranter says Avilla was in the Trapeze and Eddie says he wasn't. There was a message which Eddie couldn't deliver because Avilla wasn't there—a phone number Avilla was supposed to call." He reached in his pocket and pulled out a crumpled slip of paper. "Worth a try?" He looked around at us, then switched on the squawk box and dialed a number.

It rang four or five times and finally a male voice answered. Just a simple "Hello."

"May I ask to whom I'm speaking?" Chambrun said.

"May I ask who's asking that?" the voice said.

"I am Pierre Chambrun, manager of the Beaumont Hotel," Chambrun said. "The night before last a message was left here for Ricardo Avilla."

"So?"

"We were unable to deliver the message. I am calling to inform whoever left his number for Avilla to call."

"Thank you for telling me," the voice said. The phone went dead.

Guardino reached out and took the slip of paper from Chambrun. "The telephone company will tell us whose number that is," he said.

"So you're putting me in the same straitjacket you're in, Pierre," Hardy said. "I can't go after my killer because of the hostages."

"Not yet," Chambrun said.

"What difference are a few hours going to make?"

Chambrun gave him a grim look. "The direction the heat is coming from could change," he said.

Everybody seemed to have something special to do. Guardino was off somewhere, trying to check the telephone number Chambrun had called; Yardley was at another phone trying to make contact with Lord Huntingdon in London, in the hope that Inspector Brooks might have told his chief something useful; Hardy, I think feeling that he was stalled in his tracks by the hostage situation, had taken a couple of fingerprint experts over to the Annex. The two men who had attacked Chambrun and held him prisoner must have left traces of themselves. How useful could fingerprints be? It wasn't likely that foreign terrorists would have fingerprints on file with the police or the FBI, but Hardy wasn't a man to leave anything to chance. It could pay off later in case Chambrun wasn't able to identify the men if they were picked up later.

I was tempted beyond belief to go down the hall to my room, fall on the bed, and get some shut-eye. I had been up around the clock twice and more. Chambrun was back. All was right with our world; God was in his heaven again. But there was a little less than five hours to go now before the fate of the hostages would be decided, with a bomb threatening the building and other lives as well. Even in the condition I was in, I knew sleep would be impossible. But doing nothing was unbearable.

Chambrun indicated he didn't need me, and that the best thing I could do was keep moving around the lobby area, watch out for Avilla, and fend the press away from The Man's office. I wanted to ask him what he'd meant about the heat coming from another direction, but this didn't seem to be the right moment. I left him alone with Betsy Ruysdale, telling myself they were entitled to a moment of privacy.

Down in the lobby the clock over the front desk told me it was seven-thirty, just four and a half hours to go for the hostages. Lois was still there, watching and waiting.

"Avilla isn't going to show," I said. "He has to know that we're looking for him."

"If he's working for the people in Twenty-two B, he has to be able to report to them," she said.

"We're not so sure he's the one," I said. I told her about Chambrun and the two men in the Annex with radio equipment. As I was telling her I remembered something that nobody had commented on. When the man in Twenty-two B had made his last call to The Man's office he'd begun by saying "Welcome home." He not only knew that Chambrun had been held prisoner, but that he'd been rescued.

"Does your man in the Trapeze still say I was wrong about seeing Avilla there?" Lois asked.

I told her the police were checking out a phone number Eddie had been supposed to deliver to Avilla. "I suspect they're also checking out the Plaza Hotel, where Sanchez says he is staying. They'll either catch him there or he'll really have gone underground."

"My father doesn't have much more time, Mark." Her voice was unsteady.

"Your father and three others," I said. "We're waiting for some kind of decision from the men at the top."

"And if they decide not to give in? The murder of Inspector Brooks makes it clear what we can expect, doesn't it? They're not playing games, Mark. They mean what they say."

"I don't think Chambrun and the others who are here have ever doubted that," I said.

"So what will they do when the time comes?"

"I don't think that decision has been made," I told her.

Her hands reached out to me. "It's just not bearable—not to know," she said. "Will you tell me when they decide? Knowing that they have a plan would make it easier."

"I'll tell you when I know anything," I promised her.

"Thank you, Mark. If there was someone up there you cared about, you'd know how I feel. Anything that offers a speck of hope . . ."

I left her there, waiting and hoping. The lobby had thinned out considerably as I crossed to the entrance of the Blue Lagoon night club. I had neglected trying to catch up with my girlfriend, Sally Mills, long enough. The note she'd left me suggested she might be trying something dangerous on her own, trying to help Hilary Foster. If she'd heard about Inspector Brooks, it should have cooled her off.

Mr. Cardoza was standing by the red velvet rope that kept you out of the club if you didn't have a reservation. He looked his elegant self, in spite of last night's violence.

"Looking for your lady?" he asked. "She insisted on coming to work, though she looks a little battered."

I looked past him and saw Sally talking to a couple of customers at a far table.

"Business as usual?" I said.

Cardoza shrugged. "Regular customers only," he said. "We're not swamped, as you can see. No show without Hilary Foster, but I've got a young man who plays a pretty good jazz piano. People mostly just want to know what the score is. Incidentally, so would I."

"Join the club," I said. "There's still time for someone to come up with an answer."

"I'd like to do anything I could to help the Foster girl," Cardoza said. "One of the nicest people who ever worked for us here."

"Was getting quite a rush from one of the hostages," I said.

156

Cardoza smiled. "Señor Ortiz? I suspect you've been talking to Bobby Roth."

"Flowers, jewels, the works," I said.

"I suspect Master Roth isn't familiar with men of Spanish extraction," Cardoza said. He ought to know, I thought, being Spanish himself. "As a matter of fact Ortiz and Hilary are old friends; Washington where he worked, South America where she worked. Señor Ortiz was delighted to find someone he knew here. He played it a little more elaborately than the average American man would. He wasn't the only Latin who paid attention to Hilary."

"Oh?"

"The man you're all looking for—the picture I've seen that the police artist drew."

"Avilla?"

Cardoza nodded. "The first week she worked here, Señor Avilla came several times, bought her drinks, chatted with her. Of course he is an older man—but not too old to be interested in an attractive younger woman. Who ever is?"

"You told anyone else this?" I asked.

"Jerry Dodd, about fifteen minutes ago. He came to show me the police picture and I told him."

"Had Avilla ever been a customer before Hilary came here to work?" I asked.

"Oh, yes, a number of times over the past few years. Whenever he's in New York, I think."

"What do you know about him?"

"Down in his part of the world it depends on which side you're on," Cardoza said. "A patriot if he's on your side, a monster if he's on the other."

"So do we see him as an enemy or a friend?" I asked.

Cardoza hesitated, frowning. "You have to live in that part of the world to know who's who and what's what," he said. "Jerry Dodd asked me if I thought he could be working with those characters in Twenty-two B."

"And you told him . . . ?"

"I can only make a guess," Cardoza said. "The prisoners they want set free have all been part of the communist-sponsored revolution in Central America. What I've heard of Avilla from my friends is that he hates the communists almost more than he hates the power structure in his country."

That was exactly what Sanchez had told me.

"So your guess is that he isn't involved upstairs?"

"My guess is," Cardoza said, "that he must be very interested and concerned with what's going on. The men they're talking of setting free are his enemies. Turn them loose and he would have to fight them all over again. I understand he helped get them captured in the first place."

"So he wouldn't care what happens to the hostages?"

"A guess again," Cardoza said. "He might regret it if they were harmed, but saving them might be too big a price to pay for setting his enemies free."

"Sheldon Tranter indicated to his daughter that Avilla is the enemy," I said.

Cardoza gave me his Latin shrug. "I told you I was guessing, Mark. Mr. Tranter has spent most of his diplomatic life in Avilla's world, and knows it better than you would know your own bedroom. He is Mr. Expert with a capital E. I'd have to accept his judgment."

"If his ear is so close to the ground, it's surprising they were able to take him hostage," I said.

"It was very cleverly planned, Mark," Cardoza said. "They chose the night of the park concert. There had been riots after an earlier one. When they struck here everyone thought for the first hour that it was the same thugs who had raided Times Square after the Diana Ross show. It was a giant red herring. While we were trying to protect the hotel from vandals, key terrorists went after the hostages they wanted. Duck soup."

"I understand Tranter and Sir George Brooks and Ortiz," I said, "but why Hilary Foster?"

"Provided them with a lady in distress," Cardoza said. "There would be public clamor to make a deal for her safety. Also, she had Hispanic friends, might see somebody she knew taking part."

"Roth thinks Raul Ortiz is the villain and that he arranged to have Hilary taken so he could have his sexual way with her," I said.

"Roth is a very nice but idiotic young man," Cardoza said.

Sally Mills had spotted me and I made my way across the room toward her. The young man at the piano was grinning at me and I realized he was playing an old jazz tune for my benefit, "Insufficient Sweetie!"

"The piano player's got your number," Sally said, as I got to her.

"I'm sorry, love," I said. "I don't have to tell you things have been a little crazy."

"I know." Her hand reached out to touch me.

"I found your note and it made me nervous. I was afraid you'd do something foolish."

"I didn't have the guts," she said.

"What did you have in mind?" I asked, smiling at her.

"Human-fly act down the outside of the building; just knock on the door and tell them to stop being foolish."

"You heard about Inspector Brooks?"

She shuddered, nodded. "I decided the best thing I could do for Hilary was to help restore order down here," she said. "Leave it to the people who know how to come up with something more sensible than I have."

"Smart girl," I said, and patted her cheek.

"What will they do, Mark?"

"They've still got a little more than four hours to come up with solutions," I said, avoiding a direct answer to her question. Hell, I didn't have one!

"When it's over . . . ?"

"We'll either celebrate or mourn," I said.

"It can't be—that they'll do what they threaten," she said.

"I wish I was Pollyanna," I said.

There was a council of war going on in Chambrun's office when I returned there. Chambrun, a stone statue at his desk, was listening to Guardino, Lieutenant Hardy, Yardley, a uniformed cop who turned out to be a bomb squad expert, and, of course, Betsy Ruysdale.

Yardley was talking as I walked in. "My guess is," he was saying, "that some time before midnight the powers that be will decide to load those eight prisoners on a plane and fly them to wherever they want to be taken. Public opinion would be too outraged if they were to just write off the hostages. They are too important, even the girl."

"So then?" Chambrun asked in a flat, cold voice.

"They release the hostages," Guardino said.

"And what happens to the men who've been holding them?" Chambrun asked.

"We turn them loose," Guardino said. "If we let the prisoners go we might as well let them go."

"Will they believe us if we promise them that?" Chambrun asked. "Should they believe us? Would you let them go without trying to identify them, name them, Guardino?"

"It would be a temptation," Guardino said. "But if the big shots are going to throw in the towel, we might as well throw it in all the way."

"If I were one of them, I wouldn't move an inch without taking the hostages with me," Chambrun said. "Would I turn them loose eventually?"

"Why not?" Guardino asked. "They would have served their purpose."

Chambrun moved, as though every muscle in his body ached. "Three of the hostages, Tranter, Sir George Brooks and Raul Ortiz, are experts on Central America. The girl at least knows the area. All four of them speak the language. They have been shut up for twenty hours now with their captors. They have heard conversations between those captors, they have probably listened to dozens of phone calls. It has been pointed out that those four hostages have enough information by now to hang quite a few people if they are ever set free."

"It's not easy to hang someone when he has an army to protect him," Yardley said.

"First he has to get to the army to be protected," Chambrun said. "They'd have to get out of New York, find transportation to Central America. Their one chance would be to keep the hostages as a guarantee of safe passage. After that they and their army will dispose of them as they see fit. Like garbage, perhaps?"

"You're right, of course," Yardley said.

"You're saying we don't have a very enviable choice," Guardino said. "We don't let them go and the hostages die here and they blow up your hotel; we let them take the hostages and go and they die hundreds of miles away in a foreign country. Your choice would be to save your hotel from a bombing, Mr. Chambrun?"

"I imagine if Mr. Chambrun had a choice," Yardley said, "it would be not to have a choice."

"Amen!" Chambrun said.

"What are the chances of a raid in force working?" Lieutenant Hardy asked. "You have a front entrance, a back entrance. Two SWAT teams mounting a double attack? It's a two-door suite. Properly planned, the SWAT teams could reach the hostages within a matter of seconds after they smashed in the front and back doors."

"Let me point out one thing to you, Walter," Chambrun said. "The men up there who are holding the hostages are criminals, yes; they have murdered a man, yes; but in their minds they are also patriots with a cause. They will die for that cause. The hostages know so much now that they would threaten that cause."

"A matter of seconds after the break-in, we could protect those hostages," Hardy said.

"It's a fantasy, Walter, but picture if you will a man sitting with his finger poised over a button or his hand resting on a plunger. The first sound of an attack on a very solid door and the finger touches the button or the hand pushes the plunger, and both the hostages and their captors—and my hotel—will be blown to pieces. There won't be seconds after a break-in, Walter. Not only will everyone in Twenty-two B be dead, but also the SWAT team standing outside the doors. Is that a risk you would take if you could give the orders?"

No one spoke for a moment, but Lieutenant Hardy isn't a man who gives up easily. He turned to Yardley. "Your people are endlessly busy down in Central America, Yardley. Covert operations, you call them. You must have scores of men down there. If we let the terrorists go from here, taking the hostages with them, couldn't your people save them when they got there?"

All vestiges of good humor had faded from the CIA man's face. "If they ever got there, it's possible," he said. "So we let them go, put them on a plane—with the hostages—and send them off to their people, their army. The hostages know too much. What simpler way to dispose of them than to drop them from a few thousand feet into the ocean?"

"Checkmate!" Chambrun said. "Damned if you do and damned if you don't."

The little red light blinked on Chambrun's phone. Betsy was at the sideboard getting coffee, so Chambrun picked it up himself. The squawk box was still on so we could all hear the call.

"Pierre Chambrun's office," The Man said.

"It's Jerry, Boss," Jerry Dodd's voice came through. "There's a gentleman here in the lobby who has asked me to bring him up to see you."

"Who is he?"

"He says his name is Ricardo Avilla."

It hit us like a jolt of electricity.

"*He* wants to see *me?*" Chambrun said, rising from his chair as he spoke.

"He put it a little differently," Jerry said. "He says he thought you wanted to see him."

"Bring him up, Jerry. And carefully!"

Perhaps I was too tired for anything to make sense. Ricardo Avilla, knowing that the police, the hotel security, and even the CIA were looking for him, walking into the hotel voluntarily and asking for Chambrun?

Everyone seemed to be suddenly in a kind of confused

action. Chambrun was demanding to have Mrs. Haven and Lois Tranter brought here to his office. Guardino, believe it or not, was examining a gun he had taken from a holster under his arm. I hadn't guessed he was armed. Yardley was at the phone. Betsy had gone on the run to find the two women Chambrun wanted. I just stood there like a dummy.

"I also want Eddie Walsh up here," Chambrun said to me.

"Identification?" I asked.

"You think the man with Jerry may not be the Avilla we're interested in?" Chambrun asked.

"It doesn't make sense, his coming here," I said.

Chambrun gave me his tight little smile. "Doing the unexpected is the way you win ball games like this one," he said.

I went to the outer office, got Eddie on the phone in the Trapeze, and told him he was wanted on the double. I had just turned away from the phone when Jerry Dodd appeared in the hall door. With him was a tall, dark, rather handsome man, a sprinkling of gray at his temples. I looked closely and saw the little scar below his eye that Sanchez had mentioned and that wasn't in the police artist's drawing.

"This is Mark Haskell, hotel public relations," Jerry said. "Mr. Avilla. The boss told me to bring him up."

The man gave me a pleasant smile. "I know Mr. Haskell by sight," he said.

"Mr. Chambrun's waiting for you," I said.

We walked into the inner room. Chambrun was at his desk. Guardino was standing just behind him, his right hand held up by his left coat lapel. Yardley had positioned himself so that he was behind us as we walked into the room.

"This is Mr. Ricardo Avilla," Jerry said.

"What can I do for you, Mr. Avilla?" Chambrun asked.

The man smiled. His voice was deep and pleasant. "I rather thought the question should read another way, Mr. Chambrun. Shouldn't it be, 'What can *I* do for *you?*'"

"Let me introduce these others," Chambrun said. "Mr. Guardino is—"

"New York City police," Avilla interrupted. "And Mr. Yardley is CIA. You might as well bring your gun out into the open, Mr. Guardino. It makes me nervous to see you just standing there, patting it."

Guardino let his hand drop.

Avilla looked back at Chambrun. There was nothing sinister about his smile. It was attractive. I noticed that he kept his own right hand in his jacket pocket.

"I have to admit your coming here is unexpected," Chambrun said.

"So that there can be no confusion," Avilla said, "I was told that you were looking for me."

"By whom?"

"I am registered at the Plaza Hotel," Avilla said, "but I have been staying on a yacht in the Hudson River boat basin for the last few days. My friend Luis Sanchez left a message for me at the hotel to call him. When I did, he told me that Mr. Haskell had been asking about me, that you were circulating a police artist's drawing of me, based on a description of me given him by Miss Lois Tranter. If you wanted me that badly I thought I'd better come here and check with you."

"A yacht?" Sam Yardley asked.

"My friend David Romberg keeps it at the boat basin. I have been his guest there for the last five days. You can ask him, of course."

"Romberg is the millionaire arms manufacturer," Yardley said to the rest of us.

"You have been staying in seclusion on a yacht for the last five days?" Chambrun asked.

"Oh, no. I've been coming ashore every day, attending to the business that brings me here," Avilla said. "I have spent the evenings on his yacht with David."

"So you know what's going on here?"

Avilla's smile broadened. "Doesn't the whole world?"

"Do you have some kind of ID on you, Mr. Avilla?" Guardino asked. "A passport, perhaps?"

Before Avilla could answer, the far door opened and Betsy Ruysdale appeared. With her was Mrs. Victoria Haven, tall, elegant, tense. Avilla turned and saw her.

"My dear Mrs. Haven!" he said.

Mrs. Haven opened her purse, took out her glasses, and put them on. Her eyes widened behind the lenses. "Extraordinary!" she said. "He looks almost exactly like a man I knew forty-five years ago—Carlos Avilla."

Avilla did a strange thing. He took his right hand out of his pocket, placed each hand stiffly against his thighs and stood there like a kid about to recite something. And that's exactly what he did.

"'Here is Edward Bear, coming down the stairs now, bump, bump, bump, on the back of his head, behind Christopher Robin. It is, as far as he knows, the only way of coming downstairs . . . Anyhow, here he is at the bottom, and ready to be introduced to you. Winnie-the-Pooh.'"

Mrs. Haven's face relaxed in a joyful expression. "Ricardo!" she said.

Avilla crossed over to her, took both her hands in his,

bent down and kissed them both in an old-world gesture. I saw that he wore a black glove on his right hand. He turned, smiling at all of us.

"Many years ago Mrs. Haven taught me my first English," he said. "We began with A. A. Milne's classic children's book. I have never forgotten the first paragraph of *Winnie-the-Pooh*. Forty-five years and it has stayed with me all that time."

The room was crowding up. Lois Tranter had come in the room and was standing by the door staring at Avilla. Eddie Walsh came in just behind her.

"You sent for me, Mr. Chambrun? Oh, hi, Mr. Avilla."

"Hello, Eddie," Avilla said.

"There was a message for you but you never came in to get it," Eddie said. "Night before last. A phone number. I gave it to Mr. Chambrun."

"Thanks, Eddie," Avilla said. "It probably wasn't important. Ship-to-shore phone number."

Chambrun broke into the chitchat. "Miss Tranter?" was all he said.

Lois Tranter's face had lost all its color. "That is the man my father pointed out to me in the Trapeze Bar the night before last. He is the man my father said was Ricardo Avilla."

"I am flattered that you remember me from somewhere, Miss Tranter," Avilla said. "I understand you are responsible for the extraordinary likeness the police artist was able to make of me. But you are mistaken about seeing me in the Trapeze the night before last. I wasn't there. I was on a yacht in the boat basin with my host and some of his friends."

"He wasn't in my bar," Eddie said, giving Lois Tranter a "so there!" look.

Avilla, still holding one of Mrs. Haven's hands, turned to

167

Chambrun. "I'm afraid I don't understand what the concern is about my being in the Trapeze the night before last. I wasn't there, and if it matters, I can produce witnesses who can testify that I wasn't there."

"And the next night?" Guardino asked.

"The night of the excitement here?" Avilla asked. "Playing bridge with David Romberg and two of his friends."

"On the yacht?"

"On the yacht." Avilla looked down at Mrs. Haven. He was tall enough to look down at a tall lady. "Our bridge game was just ending, about two in the morning, when one of the ship's officers came into the card room to tell us what was happening here. We turned on the ship's television and watched and heard about the turmoil here." He turned back to Mrs. Haven. "I was shocked to hear that someone had attacked you, dear lady. I called the hotel immediately to find out about your condition. I may say it took forever to locate someone who could tell me anything not hysterical. I was finally assured that you were not seriously hurt."

"Just a scratch," Mrs. Haven said.

"Very high up on my agenda is to find the man responsible for that, dear lady, and deal with him privately," Avilla said. "I won't require the kind of evidence Mr. Guardino would need."

Sam Yardley got into the act at that point. "Let's say for the moment, Avilla, that you could be lying."

Avilla smiled at him. "It's your job to think that way, isn't it, Mr. Yardley?"

"I don't have to tell you, Mr. Avilla, that when you are dealing with terrorists you have to consider every alternative."

"I conceed," Avilla said, his smile widening. "Let's say, for the moment, that I could be lying."

"David Romberg sells arms and tanks—who knows what else?—to armed forces in Central America, of any side or country. Over the years, Avilla, you have probably done a great deal of business with him—automatic weapons, tanks, ammunition. You probably plan to continue dealing with him in the future."

"I will agree, so that you can complete your theory, Mr. Yardley."

"If you needed someone to provide you with an alibi, David Romberg would be a likely candidate. He sells to both sides, he cares for no man or cause but himself. It would not be to his advantage to lose a good customer like you."

"Specially with Russian money behind you," Guardino said.

Avilla's smile evaporated. "Would you go to bed with a poison snake, Guardino? Perhaps you would, but I would not." He looked at Chambrun. "Would you mind telling me why it's important whether or not I was in the Trapeze Bar night before last?"

"Only that Miss Tranter says you were and Eddie Walsh says you were not," Chambrun said.

"And you think one of them is not telling the truth?"

"Not necessarily," Chambrun said. "Miss Tranter's father could have pointed out someone who looks like you, been mistaken."

"And then she could give the police artist an exact description of the man?" Guardino asked. "Not very likely, is it?"

"Then Eddie and I are lying?" Avilla asked.

"You for your own reasons," Guardino said. "The bartender could be bought."

"Now just a minute, Buster!" Eddie said.

"Shut up, Eddie," Chambrun said quietly. "I know you're telling the truth as you know it."

"Would you like to tell me why I should lie about not being at the Trapeze night before last, Guardino?" Avilla asked. "I have been a regular customer there for the last few weeks. Nothing extraordinary happened there the night before last. Why should I deny being there if I was?"

"I don't know why, but I think you are," Guardino said. "Miss Tranter couldn't have described you so accurately if you weren't the man her father pointed out to her."

"And I say he wasn't there!" Eddie Walsh said.

The music goes round and round, I thought.

"We're wasting time on this point which we don't seem to be able to resolve," Chambrun said. "Let me lay it on the line for you, Avilla. We believe that the men holding the hostages in Twenty-two B have someone on the outside who is keeping them in touch with what's going on here in the hotel. When we knew you were here, circulating, thanks to Miss Tranter, we thought you might be that outsider."

"Romberg's yacht could be equipped with sophisticated radio equipment," Guardino said. "Could that explain why Avilla has been spending his evenings there? So he could make contact with his friends without being molested?"

"Two men in the Annex had such equipment and were using it," Chambrun said. He told Avilla briefly about his experience there. "You must know, Mr. Avilla, involved or not, who these people in Twenty-two B are."

"Who they are—faces and names—no," Avilla said. "Who they represent, yes. They are part of a so-called revolutionary group, sponsored by the Russians, who wish to overthrow existing powers who are supported by your government."

"And you and your family have been part of a revolutionary group who have been trying to overthrow governments for half a century," Yardley said.

"I am afraid you are unable to see any colors, Mr. Yardley, but black and white," Avilla said. "Or red and red-white-and-blue. My family has been interested in true democracy ever since I can remember. We have only been interested in the common man, the ordinary citizen. That is the color we follow, the color of sunshine, and free air, and no slavery. You can give that color a name if you like. I know if it pleases you to think we are communists, if it suits your purposes, you will put that name to us. If, on some other occasion it suits you to think of us as being on your side, you will call us true democrats. We, the Avillas, have always been on the side of freedom for the real people in our world."

"A nice speech," Guardino said. "We should all stand and cheer, I suppose."

"Your family has a history of the same kind of hostage-taking that is going on here," Chambrun said. "Mrs. Haven can vouch for that."

"Ah, yes," Avilla said. "Hostage-taking is as commonplace in my world as street muggings and drug-related massacres are in yours." He smiled at Mrs. Haven. "I will never forget this brave lady's last words to my grandfather when she was being released. 'Remember to kill me if you see me again,' she said. She would see that we were punished if she ever saw us again."

"Not this boy," Mrs. Haven said.

"This boy" was now in his fifties!

"I remember telling my grandfather, after she was gone, that we needed to learn another way to come downstairs, not bump, bump, bump on the back of our heads," Avilla said, his smile back again. "I decided then that you can't help decent people by harming other decent people. I have never in my whole life held anyone hostage. I remembered Mrs. Haven."

"Bravo!" Guardino said.

"Can we get back to who the people upstairs are?" Chambrun said, with exaggerated patience.

"Let me put it to you this way," Avilla said. "The eight prisoners whose release they are demanding are all communist-supported rebels. Mr. Yardley can probably tell you even more than I can about them. The CIA must have a detailed record on each of them. I can tell you this, though. They are my enemies as well as yours."

"Tell me this," Chambrun said. "Why would they choose a place like this to hold their hostages? They have to know they have locked themselves into a trap unless we choose to unlock it for them. They could have rented a house or an apartment somewhere in the city, taken their hostages there, and we'd never have known where they were."

Avilla nodded his head, slowly. "You are, at least, asking the right questions, Mr. Chambrun."

"I trust you will give me the right answer," Chambrun said.

"Not difficult," Avilla said. "Those eight prisoners whose release they are demanding are dangerous enemies of what, I sometimes think ironically, we call the free world. If they picked up any four people on the street as hostages—Smith, Jones, Brown, Greene—there's very little chance Washington and London would even consider bargaining. It would be a dastardly crime, a horror story, but Smith, Jones, Brown, and Greene would be out of luck. Washington and London would express their regrets, probably pay some kind of reparations to the unlucky families of the dead hostages, but they wouldn't set eight dangerous enemies free. For hostages they had to get people of real importance. They have done just that; an important British diplomat, the chief peace negotiator for the Organization of American States, a key member of the State Department, and a famous woman entertainer. The big governments have to hesitate about their being wiped out. The hostage-takers have something real to bargain with."

"That doesn't explain the risk of using this hotel as a place to hold them," Chambrun said.

"You're not thinking, Mr. Chambrun," Avilla said. "Security. Men like Tranter and Sir George Brooks and Raul Ortiz don't walk around unwatched. Moreover they, and the girl, were all together in one place. The chance of snatching them, one by one, and getting them out of the hotel to some other hiding place would be almost zero. They planned cleverly. They staged the raid on the hotel and in the wild confusion that followed they had no difficulty grabbing their victims and holding them in one place in the hotel. They'd had plenty of time to prepare. Security broke down in the confusion of the raid and in a matter of minutes they had their hostages under lock and key."

It was a reasonable answer to Chambrun's question, not that it mattered, I thought. Why they had done it wasn't important. They had done it.

"So now I come to the key question," Chambrun said. "It must be as apparent to you as it is to me, Mr. Avilla, that even if Washington and London finally agree to free eight prisoners, there is no way the people in Twenty-two B can let the hostages go. They will probably insist that we provide them and the hostages with a way out of the hotel. But they won't let the hostages go then, either. They know too much about who is who."

"I'm afraid I agree with that," Avilla said.

"So if you were in our position, Avilla, what would you do to save the hostages?"

"I would try to find a bargaining chip," Avilla said.

"I think we have one," Guardino said, his voice harsh. "We tell them we have their outside man and it's him or the hostages."

Avilla's smile had turned weary. "Meaning me, Guardino?"

"Meaning you!"

"Let me tell you something, Guardino. You tell them you have Ricardo Avilla, their outside man, and will feed him to the sharks if they don't release the hostages, you may have something. They might die laughing! If they didn't, they couldn't be more pleased to know I was in trouble and out of their hair. I am their very dangerous enemy, Mr. Guardino."

"You say!"

"I say. And I say one more thing," Avilla said. "You can threaten me, you can threaten the prisoners, and they won't turn a hair. They know you won't, you can't, it's not in your nature to kill me or them in cold blood. But if *I* threaten them—they know I cut my teeth on violence."

"Threaten them with what?" Chambrun asked.

"I wish I knew," Avilla said.

2

I thought Avilla hadn't come quite clean with us. He might not know for sure how he could threaten the people in Twenty-two B, but I thought he had an idea. What it was, I couldn't guess. His values, his world, and the values and world of those madmen upstairs were totally beyond my ability to get a handle on them.

"Don't hold back on us, Avilla," Chambrun said, and I realized that he'd been thinking along just the same lines as I had.

"You wouldn't listen to what I'm thinking," Avilla said, and his smile was totally gone now.

"Try me," Chambrun said.

"I need just a clue as to who those people are, I would get my hands on someone who matters to them—" Avilla's voice hardened. "They would believe me if I told them it was a life for a life."

"You know perfectly well we wouldn't let you carry out any such threat," Guardino said. "They'd know that, too."

Avilla appeared not to hear him. "I shouldn't have waited so long," he said. "There isn't time to do what needs to be done."

"Meaning?" Chambrun asked.

"I should go through the list of registered guests, to see who might be here that I know."

"Hundreds of guests have checked out."

"But if I came across someone from my part of the world who might be suspicious. But it would take hours to go through that list."

"There is your friend Luis Sanchez, who's barricaded in a private room downstairs," Chambrun said. "He's been here for the better part of a week. He may have seen someone who would mean something to you."

"Of course! Where do I find him?"

"You're not going anywhere alone, Avilla," Guardino said. "I'm not giving you the chance to just walk out on us."

"Come along, and welcome," Avilla said. "Bring your whole damn police force with you if you want. I'm looking for killers!"

Jerry Dodd and the two men left us and the office was silent for a moment. Mrs. Haven broke the spell.

"I think you can trust that man," she said. "I knew him as a boy and all the things that made him tick then. I don't think he's changed."

"He remembers, too, Mrs. Haven," Sam Yardley said. "'Remember to kill me.' Could he have been the one who came up on the roof the night of the raid to take Sir George Brooks, saw you, and 'remembered'?"

The old lady shook her head. "I'd feel it in my bones if that's the way it was," she said.

Lois Tranter came on stage then. "He *is* the man my father pointed out to me in the Trapeze," she said. "I know the bartender says I'm wrong, but there has to be an explanation for that."

"No way," Eddie Walsh said.

176

"If I can use your other phone, I'll try to locate David Romberg," Yardley said. "If he can provide Avilla with alibis—"

"You yourself said Romberg might be willing to cover for a good customer," Chambrun said.

"There were friends, bridge partners according to Avilla, other guests probably. The yacht's crew. Not all of them could be set up to provide alibis."

"Worth a try," Chambrun said, and Yardley took off for the outer office.

"Everyone seems to be out to clear that man," Lois Tranter said. "I'm certain he's in the conspiracy that's holding my father. All he wants to do is get somewhere he can communicate with them and tell them what you're planning."

"Then he can't do us any harm, Miss Tranter," Chambrun said, "because so far we don't have a plan and he knows it."

"This man Sanchez?"

"What about him?"

"I know, from my father, that he's one of the OAS peace negotiators. But he could be double-talking, too, couldn't he, Mr. Chambrun? He tried to persuade Mark that Avilla wasn't a likely villain. There's no way to trust anyone from that world."

"That's your father's theory?"

"That everyone wants power, no matter who you betray," Lois said.

"Maybe someone will betray the people in Twenty-two B if Avilla gets lucky," Chambrun said. "We have to take all the chances that come our way, Miss Tranter. Now if you and Mrs. Haven will excuse us—and thank you for coming."

"What do I do?" Lois Tranter cried out. "Looking for Avilla was something. Now there's nothing. My father is going to die if you don't come up with something, Mr. Chambrun."

Chambrun glanced at his watch. "We have three hours and a half, Miss Tranter," he said.

For a moment it was like family in the office; The Man, Betsy, Lieutenant Hardy, and me. Eddie Walsh had left with the two women. Hardy hadn't spoken a single word or asked a question from the moment Avilla had arrived with Jerry Dodd.

"You know, Pierre, it's possible we haven't heard a single word of truth in the last half hour," he said.

"I trust Eddie Walsh and Mrs. Haven," Chambrun said.

"Mrs. Haven didn't tell us anything except something that happened forty-five years ago and what she feels in her bones," Hardy said. "Eddie Walsh didn't see Avilla in the Trapeze the night before last, but if the place was crowded as it usually is, he could have missed him if he was only there for a few minutes."

"The girl?"

"From the information she gave the police artist, she had to have seen Avilla somewhere. But let me ask you something, Pierre. She's close to hysterical over the danger her father is in. Maybe her father had pointed out Avilla to her some other time. Night before last, he may have been talking about Avilla in the Trapeze, reminding her of a man he'd pointed out to her some other time. She could be a little off her rocker right now, you know?"

Chambrun didn't answer. He just sat staring straight ahead of him, his eyes buried deep in their heavy pouches. Finally he spoke.

178

"If Avilla is on the level, he could be our only hope," he said.

"If Guardino will stay off his back," Hardy said.

"Doing his job."

"Upstairs in Twenty-two B is a man with a gun who murdered Inspector Brooks," Hardy said. "I want him. Cop killers I really want."

"I want the four hostages safe much more than I want your killer, Walter," Chambrun said.

"If there are four hostages," Hardy said.

Chambrun turned his head in a quick jerk. "Meaning what, Walter?"

"This Raul Ortiz," the lieutenant said. "It's his suite, right? He's out of a world where a man could be on either side. He could have had plenty of time to arrange for using his quarters for a hostage-taking. The others are his friends and co-workers. He knew and admired the Foster girl. He could actually have persuaded them all to come to his suite to escape the raiders. They could have walked in, innocent as lambs to the slaughter. What do you know about him, Pierre?"

"A man of peace," Chambrun said.

"Aren't we all?" Hardy said, "until war will make us rich, or powerful, or both. You have to be a history student to understand these guys."

"Yardley should be able to tell us about Ortiz," Chambrun said, as the CIA man came back from the outer office.

"Raul Ortiz?" Yardley asked. "A clever negotiator, solidly on our side. Could be head of his country's government if we ever get him off the twenty-second floor."

"The lieutenant's been suggesting he may be the villain up there," Chambrun said.

"It's an idea that's been tossed around in my shop," Yardley said. "Only because he's native to the area, I think. I've had occasion to sit down with him, talk about his world with him, and I don't buy it."

"Avilla?" Chambrun asked. It was Avilla's alibis Yardley had been checking on the outside phone.

"I got lucky and located David Romberg," Yardley said. "He backs up Avilla all the way. The phone number Eddie had *is* a ship-to-shore from the yacht."

"His very good customer," Chambrun said.

"Romberg gave me the names of other guests present, their bridge partners on the night of the raid. They don't live in isolation out on that yacht. It's fun time, round the clock. I think the alibis will check out. Everybody won't be lying."

Chambrun glanced at his watch. "Three hours and a quarter," he said.

Yardley fished a cigarette out of his pocket and lit it. He glanced at a comfortable armchair and decided to remain standing. Like the rest of us, I think he knew that to relax for a moment could result in being overpowered by fatigue and sleep. I remember thinking I might last for three hours and after that, blackout, no matter what happened to the hostages.

"We can only wait for a final decision from Washington and London," Yardley said. "I can only say I'm grateful not to be the one who has to make it."

"It doesn't matter what they decide," Chambrun said. "They let the prisoners go or they don't. Either way, the hostages aren't going to make it unless we, here in the hotel, come up with a plan of action."

"Make a guess what their demands will be," Yardley said.

"Washington and London decide to let the prisoners go,"

Chambrun said. "The people in Twenty-two B will demand a hotel limousine, probably two, to be readied in the basement garage. They'll demand safe conduct to those cars, insist on having their own drivers. The cars are not to be followed. If they are, a dead hostage will be dumped out on the street, just to let us know they mean business."

"So we guarantee them safe conduct and the hostages get it at the other end of the line," Yardley said.

Chambrun nodded. "Washington and London decide against freeing the prisoners and we start seeing hostages go tumbling past those windows to the street."

"And when they're all gone they blow up the hotel and themselves," Yardley said. "Do you have any choice but to empty the hotel and pray?"

"Yes, damn it!" Chambrun brought his fist down on the desk. "There has to be an alternative!"

"Then you are a genius," Yardley said.

"My hotel, my guests who chose this as a safe place to stay. I don't just let it happen."

"You lead a charge and you'll be one of the first people dead," Yardley said.

"If that was the price for winning, I would pay it," Chambrun said.

I believed he meant it.

"Those are brave words, Pierre," Lieutenant Hardy said. "But making a dead hero of yourself isn't going to save anyone."

"And you are the one person they're contacting here," Yardley said. "You wouldn't be much use to us dead."

"So we keep our fingers crossed and hope that Avilla is on the level and comes up with something," Chambrun said.

"Like what?" Hardy asked.

"Some way to apply pressure from our end," Chambrun said.

"I wish I thought that was more than a hopeful dream," Yardley said.

Depending on Ricardo Avilla to save our collective necks was not exactly a cheerful prospect. All charm, a record of toughness and a planner of violence, with probably no real concern for any human life on earth except his own, no concern for anything outside his own world and his own causes. And then I found myself wondering how different that was from any other man in today's power structures all around the globe. The men toying with the destinies of the hostages in Washington and London were probably no different. They were thinking of the best course for their own purposes, politely regretting what might happen to Sheldon Tranter, Sir George Brooks, Raul Ortiz, and Hilary Foster. Nice people, the three men, devoted workers on their side, but two great nations were not going to knuckle under to threats. That would be a sign of weakness, wouldn't it? Too bad that people had to die, but you don't become spineless in the face of that. The hostages would be remembered as heroes; there would be church services attended by top dignitaries; there would be an outcry in the United Nations about atrocities committed by the left. Would we, Chambrun and the rest of us in the Beaumont, ever forget that we had sat here for twenty-four hours doing nothing, because we couldn't think of anything to do?

The red light blinked on Chambrun's phone. Betsy answered, and once again she pointed to the ceiling. Suite Twenty-two B was on the line again.

"Good evening, Mr. Chambrun," the now-familiar voice said. The squawk box was on and we could all hear.

"You've called to give me instructions," Chambrun said.

"What else, Mr. Chambrun? We are waiting, of course, to hear from the Georgia airport. When we know our friends are safely underway there, we will be halfway home."

"Getting out of here with the hostages is the other half," Chambrun said.

"Precisely. We will want—"

"You will want two hotel limousines ready in the basement garage. There will be two Lincolns with automatic drive. You will provide the drivers. You will use the service elevator to get to the cars. If the police attempt to follow you, Fifth Avenue will be littered with bodies. You will want helicopters that might follow you kept out of the air. Have I omitted something?"

"It's a pleasure to deal with you, Mr. Chambrun. There is one thing. On the way from here to the waiting cars there will be a gun at each hostage's head. One false move—"

"A question," Chambrun said. "What happens to the hostages after you get to where you're planning to go?"

"They will be released, of course."

"Up to now I have believed everything you've told me," Chambrun said. "That I don't believe."

The voice made a chuckling sound. "You are wasting your talents running a hotel, Mr. Chambrun. You have the gift for thinking just as I think. I will give you one more call at exactly eleven-thirty. You will confirm then that you have made all the arrangements, and I will let you know that I've had the right word from Georgia. If I haven't, Mr. Chambrun, I suggest you head for the nearest bomb shelter."

The phone clicked off.

Chambrun took a white linen handkerchief from his breast pocket and wiped his face with it. In spite of the air conditioning in the office, he was sweating.

"The worst of our guesses spelled out for us," Sam Yardley said.

The door at the far end of the office opened and Guardino came back with Ricardo Avilla. Avilla looked somehow changed to me. There was no smile and the lines in his face seemed to be more deeply etched.

"No luck, if Luis Sanchez is to be believed," Guardino said. "He hasn't seen anyone around the hotel whom Avilla thinks might be involved."

"That's all?" Chambrun asked.

"They did some talking in Spanish until I stopped them," Guardino said. He gave Avilla a hostile look. "No way to be sure this character didn't pull something on me."

"Tell them what you did hear," Avilla said in a flat voice.

"How they got to Twenty-two B?" Guardino said. "They played right into their hands. Made to order for them."

"You like to make that clear?" Chambrun asked.

"This Sanchez was in the lobby after the worst of the riot was over, talking to Sir George Brooks, who had come down from the roof to see what was happening. Sheldon Tranter joined them. They all know each other from the negotiations that are going on at the United Nations. Tranter said he'd just had a phone call in his room from Raul Ortiz in Twenty-two B, suggesting they all come up to his suite where they'd be safe and comfortable. Sanchez refused because he wanted to stay with his staff. But Brooks and Tranter took off. Walked right into it!"

"So it is Ortiz!" Yardley said. "He suckered them up there and had them cold!"

Avilla spoke for the first time. "I have known Raul Ortiz most of his life," he said. "I don't believe that for a moment. Can I ask you a question, Chambrun?"

"Of course."

"The voice that has been communicating with you from Twenty-two B; is there a Spanish accent?"

"No."

"Avilla, you come from a Spanish-speaking country," Guardino said, "and you don't have an accent."

"Thanks to Mrs. Haven, forty-five years ago," Avilla said. "A British accent, Mr. Chambrun?"

"No. Cultivated but not British," Chambrun said. We'd all heard the voice and he was right.

Avilla, his artificial hand jammed deep in his coat pocket, nodded slowly. "You have been looking for a man on the outside who has been communicating with the hostage-takers."

"You," Guardino said. "I think—"

"Has it occurred to any of you that it might be a woman?" Avilla interrupted. "A woman who has heard all your plans, knows exactly how you're thinking?"

Chambrun's face tightened. "There is only one such woman," he said, glancing at Betsy Ruysdale. "I can assure you—"

"There is another," Avilla said. "Miss Lois Tranter!"

"You have to be kidding!" Guardino said.

"I am from Central America," Avilla said, "so you are ready to suspect me of anything. Miss Tranter is an American girl and the daughter of a respected American diplomat so you cannot suspect her of anything."

Chambrun leaned forward in his chair. "I apologize to you, Avilla," he said. "Miss Tranter has been in and out a great deal in the last hours. She's spent some time with

185

Haskell. Has she tried to pry any sort of information out of you, Mark?"

"Of course," I said. Avilla's suggestion was absurd. "Her father is being held up there. She's out of her mind with fear for him. Of course she's asked me what you planned to do."

"Are you making the cockeyed suggestion, Avilla, that Miss Tranter is working for the people who are holding her father?" Guardino asked.

Avilla looked him straight in the eye. "I'm suggesting that she is working for her father and that he has engineered this whole disaster," he said.

Guardino laughed. He was the only one who did.

"That's pretty farfetched," Yardley said, but he sounded like a man who wanted to hear more.

"Farfetched because he is an American being accused by a spick?" Avilla said.

"I haven't been able to accept from the start that the four hostages were all taken at gunpoint up to Twenty-two B. Tranter and Brooks could not have been taken that easily. The Foster girl might have. Raul Ortiz was already up there. When Sanchez told me about the invitation to go up to Twenty-two B, I began to see how it had been managed."

"The invitation came from Raul Ortiz," Guardino said.

"That's what Tranter said. He meant to lure Sanchez up there, too. It didn't matter when that didn't work because he had enough to work with—Brooks, Ortiz, and the girl—and of course Tranter himself."

"It won't wash," Yardley said. "Tranter has an impeccable reputation, all the way up to the Oval Office."

"Which is why it has worked and will work to the bitter end," Avilla said. "Let me tell you about Sheldon Tranter."

"Oh, brother!" Guardino said. He wasn't even close to buying.

"He has spent the last twenty years of his life in my world," Avilla said. "He raised his daughter there. One of his great values to your government is that he was able to talk to both sides, the left and the right. He is one of the few Americans, except perhaps for some of Mr. Yardley's covert operators, who's had contact with the left. He could come and go at will to negotiate with them."

"So?" Guardino said.

"There comes a time when the price is high enough, when a man cannot resist temptation. Whatever his assignment was down there, Tranter must have had his own opinions about who is right and who is wrong. The price got high enough and he took it."

"Not for a minute," Guardino said.

"Someone has known exactly the right people to contact," Avilla said. "Lord Huntingdon in London, your boss in the CIA, Mr. Yardley, the top people in your State Department. No crazy revolutionary terrorist could have handled things so expertly."

"What do you suggest, Mr. Avilla?" Chambrun said.

"Something you won't agree to," Avilla said.

"Try us."

"Turn Miss Tranter over to me, let Tranter know that I've got her, and that he has to bargain with me."

"And what would you do with her?" Chambrun asked.

Avilla gave him a grim smile. "Just what he intends to do with the hostages. If Tranter won't bargain for his own daughter, then there's no way to turn him off course."

"He will know that we won't harm her," Guardino said.

"He will know that you won't," Avilla said. "He will also know that I would!"

I realize now how absurd we can be. I simply couldn't believe that a nice-looking man wearing a three-button Brooks Brothers summer suit could be seriously considering a cold-blooded murder. Let him grow a beard for a couple of days, put him in blue jeans and a dirty work shirt and you might have a different set of thoughts about him. That shows how silly our judgments about people can be. Avilla had cut his teeth on terror. No matter how civilized he looked and sounded he wouldn't hesitate a moment to take a life if it would promote his own interests.

"You would harm her?" Guardino asked, believing, yet not believing.

"I have spent a lifetime, Guardino, building a reputation. If Tranter doesn't buy it, then it doesn't matter much what I would be willing to do."

"You're not prepared to get into the act on our side because you love us, Avilla," Chambrun said.

The smile returned, but now it was tight and cold. "You're right, Mr. Chambrun. I have never had any reason to love or trust money and power. But there is a man upstairs who has devoted *his* life to the cause of peace and freedom for what you call 'the common man.' Lose Raul Ortiz and my world loses one of its few champions. I would go to any lengths to get him out of this trap."

"Of course we can't turn the girl over to you, Avilla," Sam Yardley said.

Chambrun reached for the cup of coffee on his desk which, by now, must have been stone-cold. He sipped, made a wry face, and put it down. "Would you turn her over to me, Yardley?" he asked.

"Meaning just what?" Yardley asked.

"I don't know if you have bought Avilla's theory about Tranter or not, Mr. Yardley," Chambrun said. "I think, personally, that it is good enough to test out. Bring the girl here and leave her with me and Ruysdale and Mark, who is her friend. I will set the rest of you up in the next room with the intercom turned on so that you can hear."

"What can you possibly accomplish?" Guardino asked.

"If I had to deal with a hyped-up, psychotic terrorist with a cause for which he'd give his life, I'd have to say 'nothing.' But if Tranter is at the center of this, with his daughter as an ally, I'm dealing with people who want to live to enjoy the money and the power they've been promised to do the job. If I can convince Lois Tranter that neither she nor her father can get out of this alive, that may be the bargaining chip we need."

"And if they're not involved, if this is just a ploy of Avilla's?" Guardino asked.

"I will have wasted my time," Chambrun said.

Yardley was a buyer. "Is there anything we can do to help?" he asked.

"I think so," Chambrun said. "You know the people they've been calling, Lord Huntingdon in London, the State Department here, the Organization of American States. Get through to them and tell them that when Twenty-two B calls them next they are to say that a decision about the prisoners in Georgia is about to be made, and that it looks now, in spite of their own feelings in the matter, as though that decision would be negative. The prisoners will not be set free, in spite of the hostages."

"And then, as you have said, we'll see one of the hostages go tumbling past your windows there," Guardino said.

"Let Huntingdon and the others tell them there's still hope if that doesn't happen. If it happens," Chambrun said, "then we have lost nothing. Because if we're dealing with crazy terrorists and not Tranter, the hostages are going to die anyway."

189

"It's worth a try," Yardley said. He looked at Guardino and Lieutenant Hardy. "You willing to go along?"

Hardy nodded.

Guardino shrugged. "As long as Avilla stays in my custody."

"What do you think, Avilla?" Chambrun asked.

Avilla hesitated. "If I am right, then there's one thing you've been led to believe that isn't so," he said. "Tranter will not set off a bomb while he's still in Twenty-two B. If you can keep him there, you may save your hotel, but I agree with Guardino. You may see a body or two fall past your windows."

"Maybe Miss Tranter can be persuaded to get to her father before that happens," Chambrun said.

"Set us up wherever you plan to," Yardley said. "We can't lose by trying."

It was going on ten-thirty; in an hour we'd be getting the last call promised us from Twenty-two B; in an hour and a half the ball game would be over, one way or the other.

I was assigned to find Lois Tranter and bring her to Chambrun's office. I have to admit to being in a kind of daze. I would go with Chambrun wherever he was headed, but I just couldn't see the Tranters as the key to our puzzle. I knew Tranter by sight, tall, distinguished-looking, slightly balding. I'd seen his registration card when he'd first come to the Beaumont ten days ago. A top American diplomat, an A credit rating, no bad habits like alcohol or drugs, not a woman chaser, special treatment asked for by the State Department. He didn't need money or power, he already had it. And Lois, frightened out of her wits for him, her whole life entwined with his? No way I could imagine her

190

as a spy and a traitor. But I went to find her, fighting the temptation to warn her about Avilla's suspicions before she was confronted with them.

She wouldn't be in the lobby looking for Avilla. She knew we had found him. I couldn't imagine her sitting in one of the bars drinking by herself. Then I remembered she'd thought of going to her father's room to look through his papers for some clue that might be helpful.

I went to one of the house-phones in the now almost orderly lobby and got the switchboard to ring Tranter's room on the seventeenth floor. There was no answer. I went to the front desk and asked the night clerk, who had relieved the exhausted Atterbury, for the spare key to Tranter's room. If Lois had been there, she might have left something behind that would suggest where I could find her—the name and phone number of the friends where she was supposed to be staying. Tranter would have had that among his things, probably in his wallet in his pocket, up in Twenty-two B.

The clerk couldn't give me the key because Lois had asked for it a while back. The maids on the floor would have a passkey and I went up to seventeen. When I asked the maid on night duty for the key to 1712 she told me that a young lady, the guest's daughter she understood, was in the room.

I went down the hall and knocked on the door. There was no answer at first, and then I hammered on it good and called out. "It's Mark Haskell, Lois!"

She opened the door and stood there, looking like death.

"I had to find some place where I wouldn't be swamped by reporters and questions," she said. "I couldn't leave the hotel. There might be news."

"There is news," I said, feeling like a jerk. "Chambrun wants you to come down to his office. He promised to tell you about any decisions."

"What have they decided?" She reached out to touch me.

"He'll have to tell you; I don't honestly know," I said.

"There's so little time!" she said. "Let me get my bag."

She went into the room and came back with one of those bags you carry with a strap over your shoulder. "Have they heard anything from Twenty-two B?" she asked, as we headed for the elevator.

"Only that they'd be calling at eleven-thirty with final instructions."

"Have they decided to release the prisoners?"

"I don't think there's been a final decision," I said.

She sounded tortured. "There's so little time. Suppose Dad is the first hostage they decide to harm?"

"I should think he would be their trump card," I said, "the one they'd hold for the final chance of getting their way." Double-talk that tasted bad in my mouth.

We took the elevator to the second floor. The security men there passed us through to Chambrun's office. The Man was sitting at his desk, with Betsy stationed just behind him as usual. He gave Lois an almost cordial smile of greeting.

"Thank you for coming," he said.

"Mark says there is news."

"Nothing that will be news to you, Lois," he said.

"I don't understand."

"Who has promised your father what?" Chambrun asked, as casually as if he was asking about the weather.

"I still don't understand!" Lois said.

"You and I will do a lot better, Lois, if we stop playing

games," Chambrun said. "It's taken us quite a while to get sensible about all this, but we finally made it. Who bought your father and what was he promised for engineering all this?"

She looked utterly bewildered. Was she, or was she a brilliant actress? "I honestly don't know what you're talking about," she said.

"Time is running out, Lois. So let me put it to you this way. Having discovered that your father masterminded this whole thing, the raid on the hotel, the taking of the hostages, I can assure you that he will never get off the Twenty-second floor alive unless the real hostages are set free and unharmed."

"But Mr. Chambrun, my father *is* a hostage!"

"I think not, Lois. Nor do I think you are an anxious and loving daughter, concerned for your father's safety. I think you are a scheming and conniving bitch who will deserve everything that will eventually come your way."

"Coming my way?" Her voice was suddenly a little shaky.

"Drop the game playing, my dear," Chambrun said. "We know that your father directed this whole adventure. We know that he murdered Inspector Brooks. We know that he attempted to murder Mrs. Victoria Haven. You are his accomplice in those crimes."

"Why on earth would he want to murder Mrs. Haven?"

"He went up to the roof to persuade Sir George Brooks to take cover in Twenty-two B. He hoped Sir George would go with him willingly, but if he refused, your father would have forced him at gunpoint. It is never totally dark on the roof—city lights give it a glow all night. Your father saw Mrs. Haven sitting in her garden. He didn't know two things about her so he had to eliminate her. He couldn't afford to have her be a witness against him."

"Two things he didn't know?"

"That Mrs. Haven can't see beyond the end of her nose without her glasses, and that she isn't a busybody— couldn't care less who might be visiting Penthouse Three. Your father missed killing her by inches. Then the hysterical little dog started barking, and Sir George charged out of his penthouse, armed and ready for action. Your father couldn't risk that kind of encounter. One of them might not survive. He had to wait until later to get Sir George down to Twenty-two B."

"What *is* going to happen to me, Mr. Chambrun?" Lois asked, her voice quite steady now.

"Your father will have to make the decision," Chambrun said.

"Decision about what? I don't understand—"

"He is going to have to decide whether you live or die, Lois. If he cares enough for you it will go one way, if he doesn't care enough for you it will go the other."

"I think I must be dreaming, or you have gone mad, Mr. Chambrun!"

"Academy Award," Chambrun said.

"What?"

"A prize for acting," Chambrun said. "Let me tell you how it is going to be. This time, when your father calls here, *I* will provide the ifs, ands, and buts. Depending on what he is prepared to do about Raul Ortiz, Sir George Brooks, and Hilary Foster, you will live or die. Frankly, if I were in your father's shoes I might choose to die. He will never again find any place in the world where he can live in safety. His communist friends won't help him because he will have failed them. The eight prisoners won't be set free, you know."

Lois opened her handbag and took out a tissue with

which she blotted at the little beads of perspiration on her upper lip. She put the tissue back and when her hand came out again she was holding a small handgun aimed directly at Chambrun. He gave her an unruffled look.

"Revenge, or hope of escape?" he asked, quite calmly. "You will make things much easier for my friend Lieutenant Hardy if you pull that trigger. Right now he can only prosecute you as an accessory before the fact in the murder of Inspector Brooks. Kill me—and he's in the next room— he's got you for Murder One, the rest of your life behind bars."

The door from Chambrun's dressing room burst open and Hardy, Guardino, and Yardley charged into the room, followed by Avilla. The three lawmen were armed.

"One second is all you've got, Miss Tranter," Lieutenant Hardy said.

It seemed like forever to me before her hand relaxed and the little pearl-handled gun she'd been aiming at Chambrun dropped noiselessly on the thick Oriental rug. Guardino dove for it and picked it up.

"What next?" Sam Yardley asked.

Chambrun smiled at him as though nothing at all had happened. "In twenty minutes the phone will ring," he said.

The twenty longest minutes of my life. There was almost no conversation as we waited. Hardy had taken Lois's bag away from her, and her wrists were handcuffed together. She sat rigid, motionless, in a chair by Chambrun's desk, her face the color of ashes.

"You're counting on a civilized reaction from Tranter?" Yardley asked at one point. "He will give himself up to save his daughter?"

"When you have been bitten by a rabid dog you sometimes go mad yourself," Chambrun said. "We have to gamble that that hasn't happened."

We waited. I found myself riveted on the little electric clock on Chambrun's desk, the second hand clicking round and round.

"She didn't confess to anything," Guardino said.

"How much more confession do you need than that gun pointed at my head?" Chambrun asked. "She didn't have to tell me that the whole ploy about Avilla was to make us look the other way."

"The radio equipment she's supposed to have used to communicate with Twenty-two B?"

"You know where that is," Chambrun said. "The two men who had me in the Annex. She circulated, listened to us talk and plan, and then passed the word to them in the crowd in the lobby. I don't need the actual machinery to know how she worked it."

Lois sat staring straight ahead of her as though she wasn't hearing anything.

At precisely eleven-thirty the red light on Chambrun's phone blinked. This time The Man didn't wait for Betsy to answer. The squawk box was on.

"Right on time, Mr. Tranter," Chambrun said.

There was a moment of silence and then the now-familiar voice. "So you've guessed, Mr. Chambrun."

"It's no longer a guess. I have your daughter here with me. In exactly ten minutes after the conclusion of this conversation she will be reunited with you."

"On what terms?"

"I will personally escort your daughter to the twenty-second floor. When the elevator door opens I will expect to find Miss Foster, Señor Ortiz, and Sir George Brooks waiting to go down with me. I will leave your daughter with you."

"Are you suggesting that if I don't buy this you will harm Lois?"

"You know better than that, Tranter, if you haven't entirely forgotten the world you grew up in. You will decide what happens to her."

"You expect me to release the hostages to you, and then you send an army up here and we all die?"

"Not at all," Chambrun said. "There are two cars waiting for you in the basement garage. You and your associates will be allowed to get to them—after I have the hostages—and you can go wherever you planned to go, unmolested by me or by the police."

Guardino made a kind of growling sound and lunged for the phone. Lieutenant Hardy blocked him, held him with one arm and clapped a huge hand over his mouth.

"You expect me to believe that?" Tranter asked.

"Try to remember this world, Mr. Tranter. I give you my word of honor that, if the hostages are safe and unharmed and in my hands, you will be free to take your daughter and your other associates up there and go your way, unwatched, unhindered."

"A schoolboy promise!" Tranter said.

"You once lived in my world, Mr. Tranter. I give you my word."

There was an interminable silence and then Tranter spoke. "Ten minutes," he said, and the phone clicked off.

"You can't do this!" Guardino shouted as Hardy released him.

"Even if Hardy has to sit on you here, Mr. Guardino, it's done," Chambrun said.

197

"And I'll sit if I have to," Hardy said.

"Don't worry, Guardino," Yardley said. "If he goes to the depths of a South American jungle, my people will find him."

"He knows that!" Guardino said.

"Now, Lois, come with me," Chambrun said. "If your beloved father really cares for you, you have a chance."

"You don't have to take her, Pierre!" Betsy Ruysdale protested. "Let someone else—"

"I have to be sure he believes me," Chambrun said.

"I will be the elevator operator," Yardley said.

How can I tell you what the next half hour was like? Betsy and I and Guardino and Hardy waited along with Avilla. Somewhere an elevator was carrying Chambrun and Lois and Yardley to the twenty-second floor. It would work, or we had seen the last of The Man. Betsy was suddenly in the protection of my arm, shaking like a leaf in a thunderstorm. There was nothing I could say to comfort her. I could only hold her tightly and pray.

As I say, it seemed like forever, and then the far door opened and Hilary Foster walked in, followed by Sir George Brooks and Raul Ortiz. Chambrun and Yardley were just behind them. I think I heard Lieutenant Hardy let out a great shout of relief.

Tranter had bought it, and he and his daughter and his co-conspirators were out into a world that would never forgive them or forget them.

Yardley, after an urgent call to the airport in Georgia, telling them that the hostages were safe and the prisoners could be returned to their jails, told us what had happened.

"We went up in the elevator, Chambrun holding the girl from behind." Yardley laughed. "That elevator moves so damn fast and every inch of the way I wished I hadn't stuck my neck out. It was possible I might never be coming down again." He glanced at me. "I think your boss had me mesmerized."

"Girl talk at all?" Hardy asked.

"Not a word," Yardley said. "I think she was just as uncertain as I was about what could happen. As the car stopped at Twenty-two I reached for the gun in my holster. Chambrun grabbed my wrist. 'I gave my word,' he said. 'Press the button marked OPEN.' I pressed the button and the car door opened. There were the three people we'd come for, Brooks, Ortiz, and Miss Foster. Standing right behind them was Tranter. I could have shot the bastard dead in his tracks."

"Why didn't you?" Guardino asked.

Yardley gave him an odd little smile. "Chambrun had given his word. I couldn't make a liar of him. The girl walked out to her father, the hostages walked into the car. Tranter, looking like a death's-head, spoke the only words. 'I'm glad I remembered your world correctly, Mr. Chambrun.' I pressed the button marked CLOSE, and here we are."

Chambrun and Betsy had drifted away into his private room. The three hostages were all talking at once, naming names, describing what the long siege had been like. Avilla was in an urgent huddle with Raul Ortiz, gabbling away in Spanish. There would be hours of debriefing these hostages for every conversation they'd overheard, every detail of their long imprisonment. The bomb squad was already at work on Twenty-two B.

"Thank heaven Chambrun guessed right about Tranter," Yardley said. "I don't think I would have risked it."

"Over the years I've learned to trust his guesses," Hardy

said. He gave me a wry smile. "Is there some hard liquor somewhere in this gilded palace, Mark? I have a feeling everybody here could stand a good stiff slug."

I looked around for Betsy, but she and Chambrun were having a private moment they needed in the next room.

Hardy put his hand on Guardino's shoulder. "Sorry I had to play rough with you, Mr. Guardino. All this has cost you is time, because we will catch up with them sooner or later, no matter where they try to hide. And Chambrun has saved three lives."

Guardino seemed to relax, and he actually smiled at Hardy. "All is forgiven, Lieutenant," he said.

Suddenly, all I cared about was bed.